Contents

T0344330

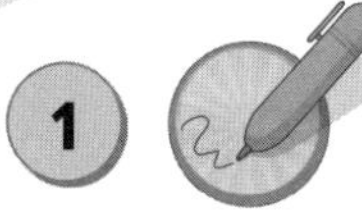

1 Write and match.

1 He's 10. He has blond hair. He likes films. His name is Oliver.

2 She's 9. She has black hair. She loves Finley Keen. Her name is ______.

3 He has black hair. He's a film star. His name is ______.

4 He has blond hair. He's wearing a red jumper. His name is ______.

2 Draw or stick a picture of yourself and a friend. Then write.

My name's ______.

I am ______ years old.

I like ______.

My friend's name is ______.

______ is ______ years old.

______ likes ______.

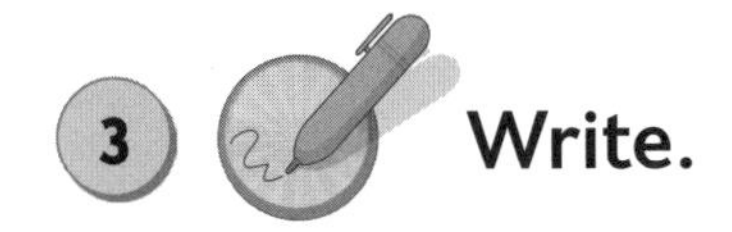

3 Write.

1 My name's Oliver. I've got glasses and green trainers. I've got a blue T-shirt.

2 My name's Sophie. ____________ a yellow T-shirt, a blue ____________ and pink trainers.

3 I'm Finley Keen. I've got a yellow scarf, a brown ____________ and black ____________.

4 My name's Uncle James. ____________ a red jumper, blue ____________ and blue trainers.

4 Write about yourself and your partner.

My name's ________________. I've got ________________ and

____.

My partner's name is ________________. He's/She's got ________________

and ____.

5 Listen and match.

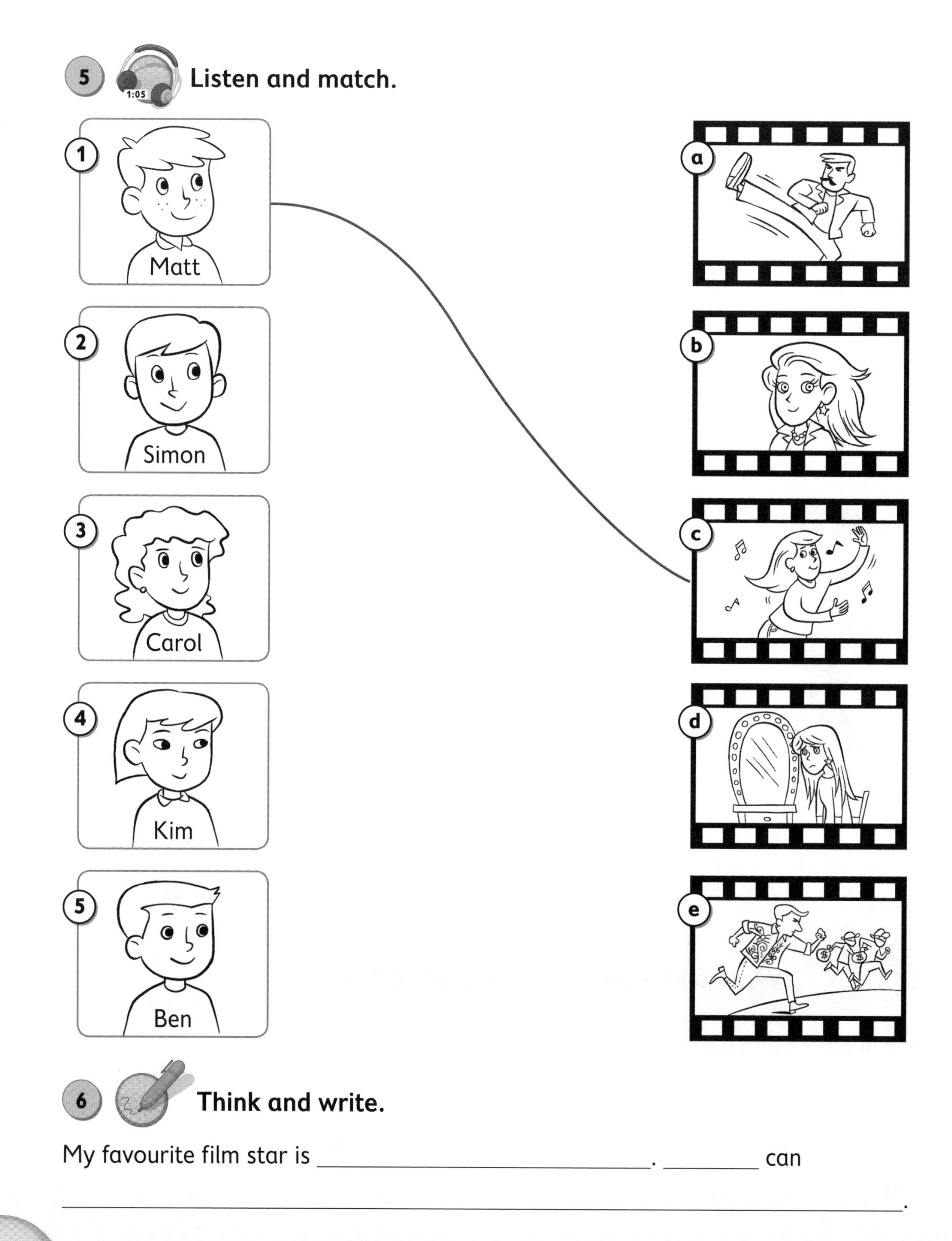

6 Think and write.

My favourite film star is ______________________. __________ can

____.

7 Listen and write the numbers.

1:09

a	84				
b					
c					
d					

8 Look and write.

50	60	70
fifty		

80	90	100

9 Write your favourite numbers.

1 My favourite number between 1 and 10 is ________________.

2 My favourite number between 10 and 50 is ________________.

3 My favourite number between 50 and 100 is ________________.

  **Read and circle.**

1 A horse is (shorter / taller) than a mouse.

2 A mouse is (bigger / smaller) than a cat.

3 A rabbit is (faster / slower) than a tortoise.

4 A cat is (smaller / bigger) than a dog.

5 A dog is (shorter / taller) than a horse.

 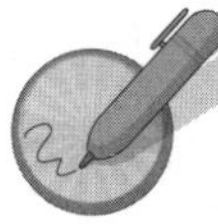 **Look and write.**

Billy

12 years old

Andy

7 years old

Sue

9 years old

Darren

11 years old

Jane

10 years old

Christine

8 years old

1 (old / young) Billy is older than Andy.

2 (old / young) Darren is ____________________ Billy.

3 (clever / young) Sue is ____________________ Christine.

4 (clever / young) Jane is ____________________ Darren.

12 Read and draw.

1 He's taller than me.

2 Her hands are bigger than his hands.

3 A mouse is smaller than a cat.

4 A rabbit is smaller than a dog.

1 Free time

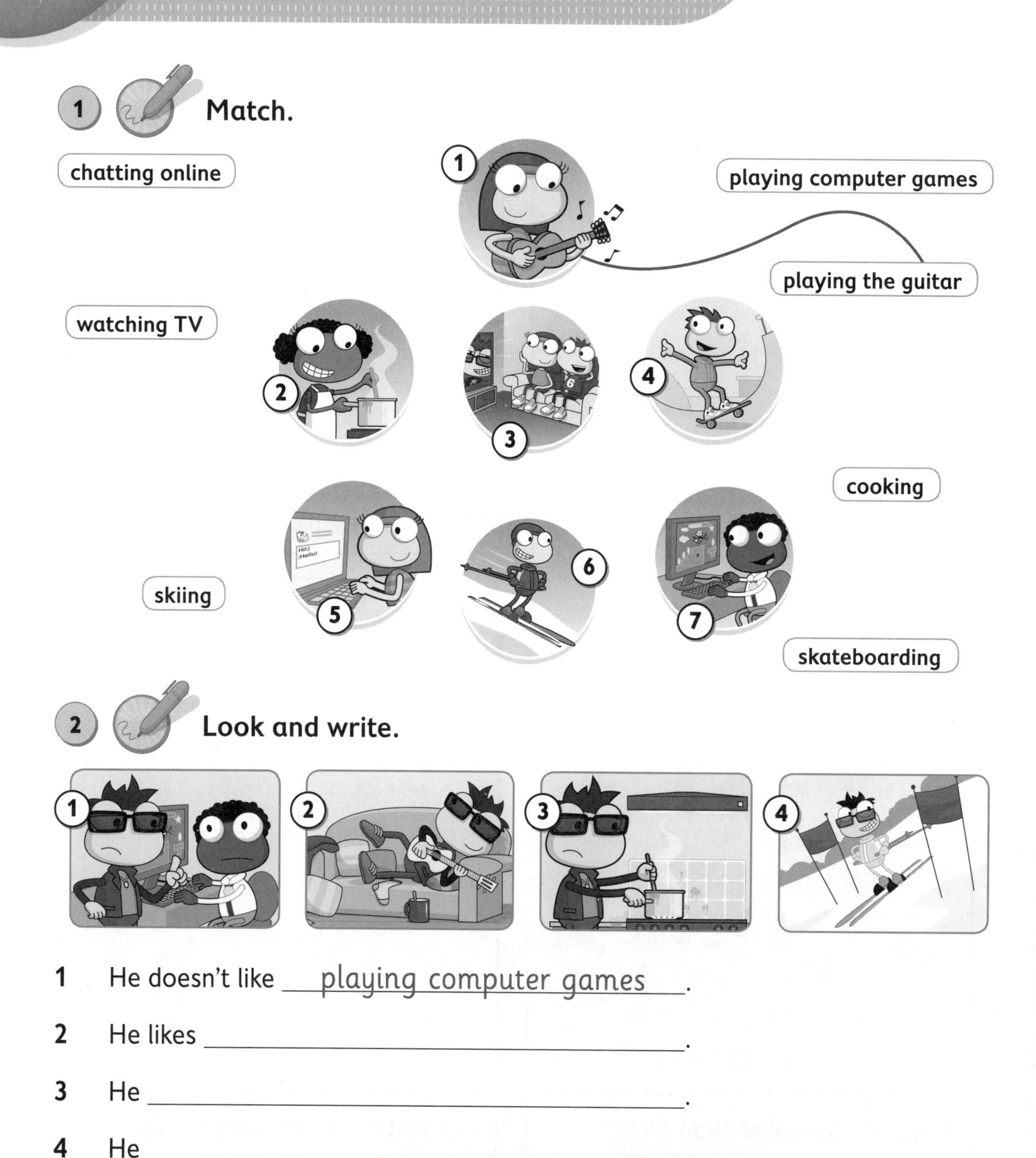

1 Match.

chatting online

playing computer games

playing the guitar

watching TV

cooking

skiing

skateboarding

2 Look and write.

1 He doesn't like playing computer games.

2 He likes ______________________.

3 He ______________________.

4 He ______________________.

3 Listen and write ✓ = likes or ✗ = doesn't like.

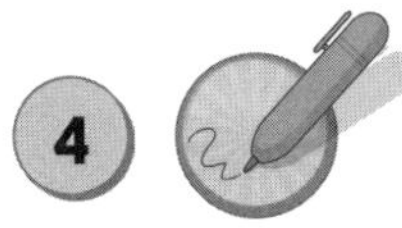

4 Look at Activity 3 and write.

1 What does Ruby like doing?

She likes skiing and ______________________.

She doesn't like ______________________.

2 What does John like doing?

He likes ______________________.

He doesn't like ______________ or ______________________.

5 Read. Then think and write.

What do you like doing?

I like ______________________.

I don't like ______________________.

  Listen and write *Y = Yes* or *N = No*.

1  Y

2 

3 

4 

 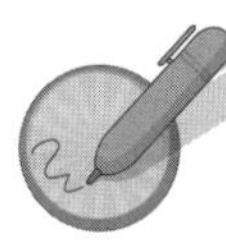 Look at Activity 6 and write.

painting	playing hockey	riding a scooter	walking the dog

1 Does she like playing hockey? Yes, she does.

2 Does he like ______? ______, he ______.

3 Do they like ______? ______, they ______.

4 Does he like ______? ______, he ______.

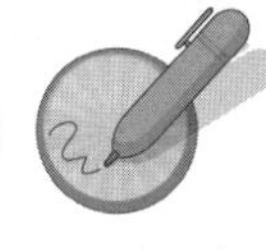 Look and write.

1 Do you like  skipping? ______, I ______.

2 Do you like  ______? ______.

3 Do you like  ______? ______.

4 Do you like  ______? ______.

9 Listen and write ✓ = likes or ✗ = doesn't like.

Fiona

Me	✓				
My mum					
My dad					

10 Look at Activity 9 and write.

1 Does Fiona like playing computer games? Yes, she does.

2 Does Fiona like watching TV? ______

3 What does Fiona's mum like doing? She likes ______.

She also likes ______ and ______.

4 What does Fiona's dad like doing? He likes ______.

He also likes ______ and ______.

11 Write questions and answers.

1

Does ______?

______

2

______?

______

12 Read. Then number the pictures in order.

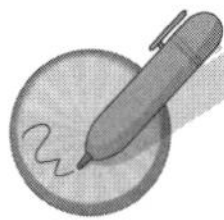

13 Look and write.

~~climbing~~
faster
jump
riding
skateboarding

1 Coco likes ___climbing___ and ______________.

2 Sophie loves ______________ a scooter.

3 Sophie and Oliver are ______________ than Coco.

4 But Coco can ______________!

PHONICS

ou ow

14 Read the words. Circle the pictures.

15 Listen and connect the letters. Then write.

1:29

1	b	ear	___
2	ch	ay	___
3	d	oy	boy
4	y	air	___

16 Listen and write the words.

1:30

1 out 2 ___ 3 ___ 4 ___

17 Read aloud. Then listen and check.

1:31

It's wintertime. The wind blows and black clouds are low. There is a lot of snow. Wear a coat, a hat and a scarf when you go out.

18  **Read and write *T = True* or *F = False*.**

① **Kelly's blog**

Hi, I'm Kelly. I'm from Canada. It's snowy here in winter. I like skiing. It's fun. I can go very fast and jump very high! Do you like skiing?

Kelly, 9, Canada

② **Tumelo's blog**

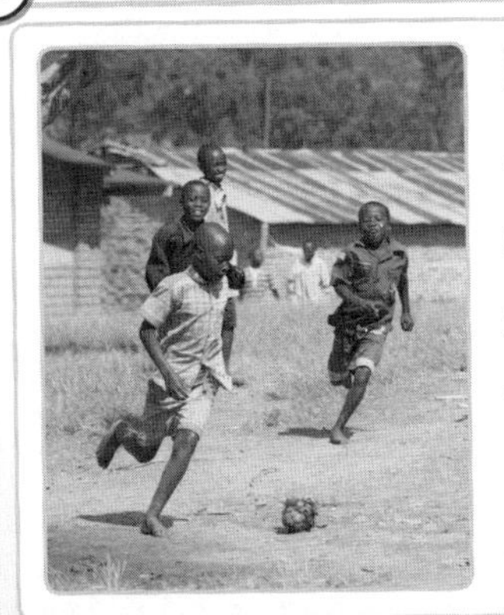

Hi, I'm Tumelo. I'm from South Africa. I like playing football at school with my friends. I can see the Soccer City stadium from my house. It's really big. My favourite team is the Mamelodi Sundowns.

Tumelo, 9, South Africa

1 Kelly likes skiing. [T]

2 Kelly can't ski fast. [ ]

3 Kelly can jump very high. [ ]

4 Tumelo likes playing football at school. [ ]

5 The stadium is not very big. [ ]

6 His favourite football team is the Mamelodi Sundowns. [ ]

19 

Listen and read. Then write.

20 Listen and tick (✓).

1:35

21 

Draw or stick a photo of a special house.

22 Look and write.

Across →

1 WALKING

3

5

7

Down ↓

2

4

6

8

23 Look. Then read and write.

~~playing computer games~~ ✓ skiing ✗ riding a scooter ✗ watching TV ✓

1 What does she like doing? She likes playing computer games.

____

2 ____? No, she doesn't.

3 What does he like doing? ____

4 He doesn't ____.

I CAN

I can identify free-time activities.

I can ask and answer about what people do in their free time.

I can understand texts about special houses.

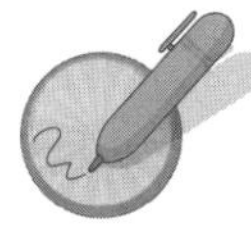

24 What do or don't you like doing? Write ✓ or ✗.

1 ☐ 2 ☐ 3 ☐ 4 ☐

5 ☐ 6 ☐ 7 ☐ 8 ☐

9 ☐ 10 ☐ 11 ☐ 12 ☐

13 ☐ 14 ☐ 15 ☐ 16 ☐

25 Look at Activity 24 and write.

I like ____

____.

I don't like ____

____.

26 Write about your friends or family.

1 My ______________ likes ______________________________.

______________ doesn't like ______________________________.

2 My ____.

____

2 Wild animals

1 

Listen and number.

a 

b 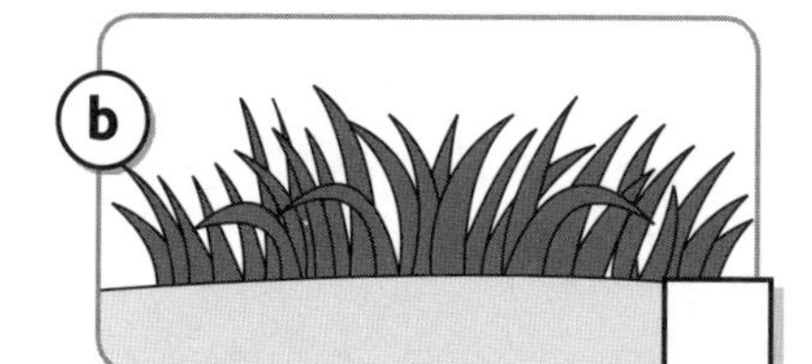

c 

d 

e 

f 

g 

h  1

2 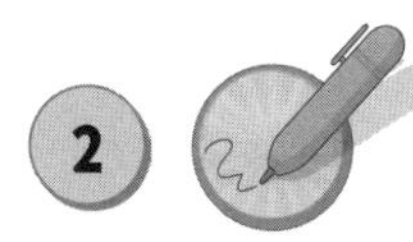 **Look and write.**

crocodile	elephant	hippo	giraffe	lion	monkey

1 

It's a lion.

2 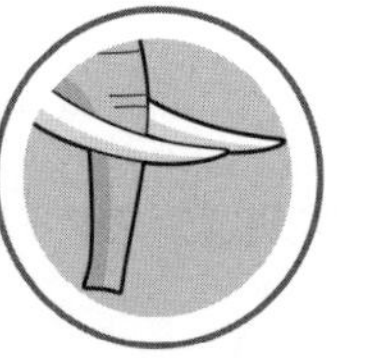

____

3 

____

4 

____

5 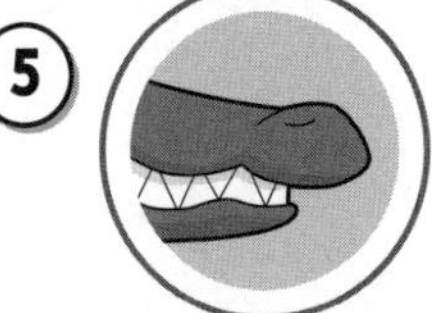

____

6 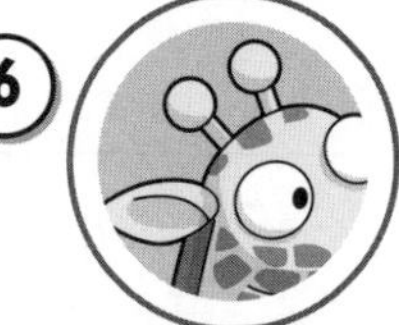

____

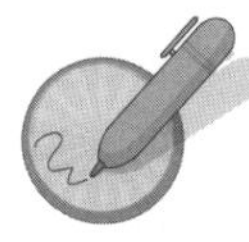

3 What do the animals eat? Write.

fruit	grass	leaves	meat

1 Monkeys eat fruit.
2 ______
3 ______
4 ______
5 ______
6 ______

4 Look. Then read and write.

	Fruit	Leaves	Grass	Meat
Monkeys	✓	✗	✗	✓
Lions	✗	✗	✗	✓
Elephants	✓	✓	✓	✗
Crocodiles	✗	✗	✗	✓

1 Do monkeys eat fruit? Yes, they do.

2 Do lions eat leaves? ______

3 ______ elephants ______ fruit? ______

4 ______ crocodiles ______? ______

5 ______ ______

5 Match.

6 Unscramble and write. Then number.

1 oferts ➡ forest
2 evrir ➡ ______
3 lsgasrand ➡ ______
4 tesedr ➡ ______
5 rernfoista ➡ ______

7 Listen and write.

1 Zebras live in ______.

2 ______ live in ______.

3 ______ live in ______.

  **Look. Then read and write.**

~~Camels~~ fast Pandas playing slowly Zebras

1 ___Camels___ eat grass. They drink very little water. They can run fast but they walk __________. They can walk all day.

2 __________ eat bamboo, leaves and insects. They like __________ with their friends. They can eat 38 kilos of food every day.

3 __________ eat a lot of grass and leaves. They drink water from rivers. They run very __________. They've got black and white stripes.

9 **Look at Activity 8 and write.**

1 What do camels eat? They eat ___grass___.
How much water do they drink? ___They drink very little water.___
Can they run fast? __________

2 What do __________? They eat __________.
How many kilos of food can they eat? __________
Do they like playing with their friends? __________

3 What do __________? They eat __________.
How much grass do they eat? __________
Can they run fast? __________

10  Read. Then number the pictures in order.

a

b

c

d

e

f

11 Read and circle.

1 The animal keeper (knows / doesn't know) where Coco is.

2 The giraffe is eating a (magazine / page from the script).

3 Sophie sees some (bananas / meat) in the rainforest.

4 Uncle James falls into some (paper / fruit) at the end of the story.

12 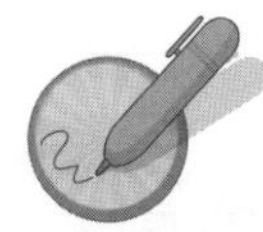 Where do the animals live? Write.

forests	grasslands	rivers

1 Elephants live in grasslands and __________.

2  ____________________

3 ____________________

PHONICS all aw

13  Read the words. Circle the pictures.

~~claw~~ draw wall yawn

14 Listen and connect the letters. Then write.

1	th	i	n	er	______
2	d	a	b	er	______
3	s	u	nn	k	thank
4	c	ow	mm	oy	______

15 Listen and write the words.

1 all 2 ______ 3 ______ 4 ______

16  Read aloud. Then listen and check.

Welcome to the zoo. Look at the big cats! They've got sharp teeth and sharp claws. I'm glad the wall is tall. You cats can't eat me for dinner!

17  **Look. Then read and answer.**

I'm Akeyo. I live in the Serengeti National Park in Tanzania. The sun shines most days here and it's very hot. There are a lot of different animals in the park. I like the giraffes. They're tall and they've got long necks. They eat the leaves at the top of the trees.

Akeyo, 10, Tanzania

1. Where does Akeyo live?
   She lives in the Serengeti National Park in Tanzania.
2. Are there many different animals in the park? ______________
3. What animals does she like? She likes ______________.
4. What do they look like? They're ______________ and they've got ______________.
5. What do they eat? ______________

18 Read and write.

Kinds of animals

Herbivores	**Carnivores**	**Omnivores**
(eat plants)	(eat other animals)	(eat plants and animals)
horses	dogs	bears
rabbits	cats	monkeys
elephants	lions	pigs
cows	tigers	mice
	snakes	

1 <u>Herbivores</u> are animals that eat <u>plants</u>. Some herbivores are horses, ________, ________ and cows.

2 ________ are animals that eat ________. Some carnivores are dogs, cats, lions, ________ and ________.

3 ________ are animals that eat both ________ and ________. Some omnivores are bears, monkeys, ________ and ________.

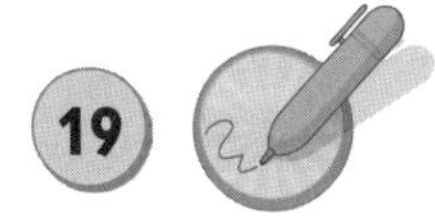

19 Look at the food chain. Write.

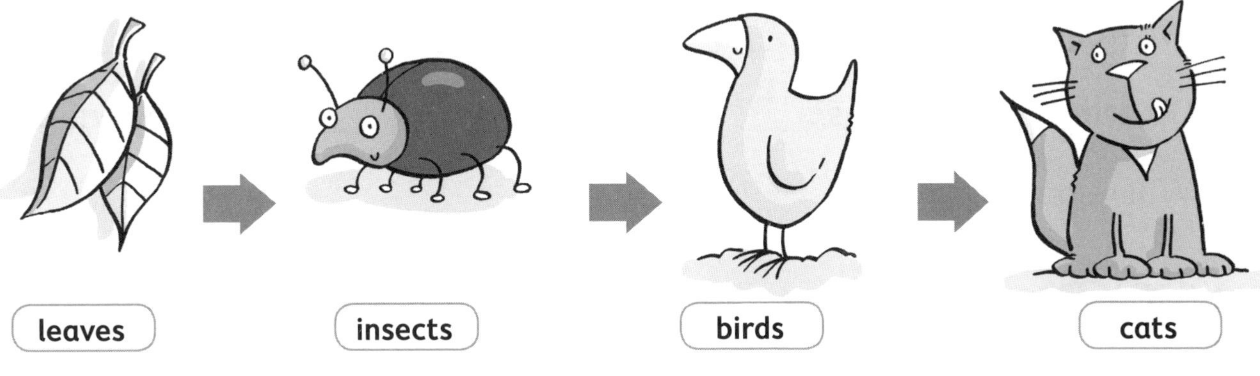

Insects eat <u>leaves</u>, birds eat ________ and cats eat ________.

I CAN DO IT!

20 Write the animals' names. Then match.

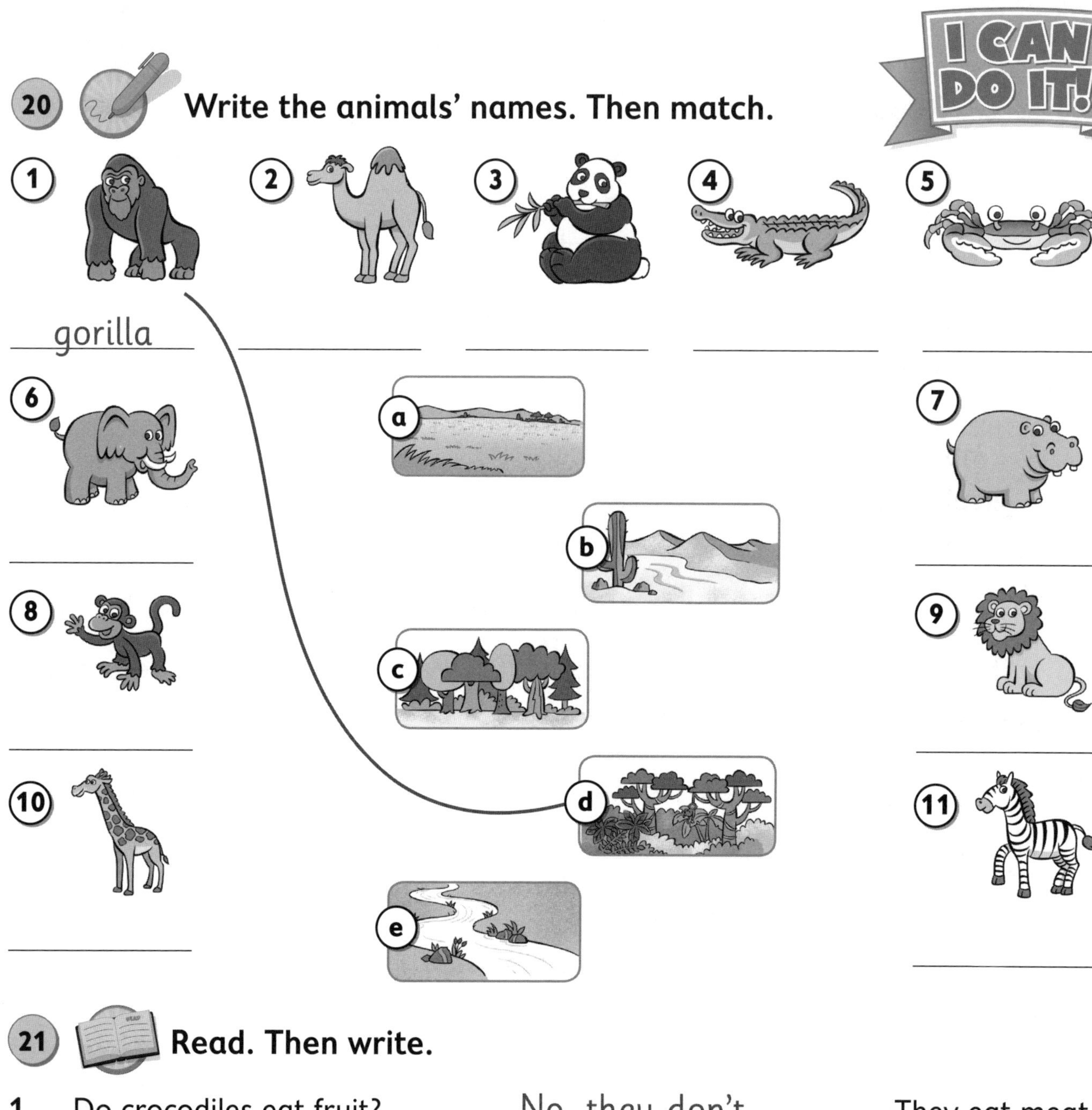

21 Read. Then write.

1 Do crocodiles eat fruit? No, they don't. They eat meat.

Where do crocodiles live? ______________________

2 Do zebras eat bananas? ______________________ They eat grass.

Where do zebras live? ______________________

I can identify wild animals, food and habitats.
I can ask and answer about what animals eat and where they live.
I can understand texts about the food chain.

Draw or stick a photo of an animal. Then write.

Grassland	River
______ live in ______.	______ live in ______.
They eat ______.	They eat ______.
They can ______.	They can ______.
They can't ______.	They can't ______.
They walk ______.	They swim ______.

Desert	Near my town
______	______
______	______
______	______
______	______
______	______

3 The seasons

1 Match.

2 Look at Activity 1. Then read and write.

Hello, everybody. What's the weather like today? Here in the north, it's [1] ___warm___. The temperature is [2] ________ degrees. Don't forget your hat!

Let's look at the east now. It's [3] ____________ today. The temperature is [4] ______________________.

Now, let's see the west. It's [5] __________ today. It's cool. The temperature is [6] ______________________.

In the south the weather is [7] ____________. There's [8] ____________ and [9] ____________. It's [10] ______________________.

3 Listen and number.

(a) 

(b) 

(c) 
1

(d) 

(e) 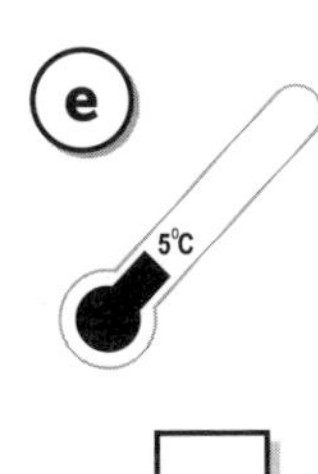

(f) 

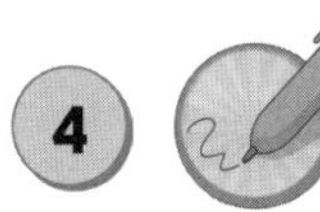
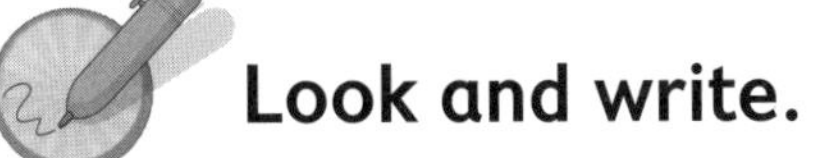

4 Look and write.

1 What's the weather like today?

There's thunder and lightning.

2 What's the weather like today?

It's ______________________.

3 What's the weather like today?

It's ______________________.

4 What's the weather like today?

It's ______________________.

5 What's the temperature today?

It's ______________________.

6 What's the temperature today?

It's ______________________.

 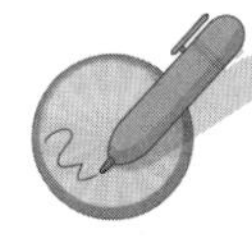

Look and write.

~~autumn~~ spring summer winter

1 

2 

3 

4 

It's autumn. It's ________. It's ________. It's ________.

6 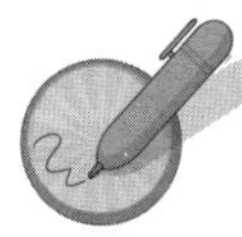

Look and write.

go camping go hiking ~~go snowboarding~~ go water skiing

1 

go snowboarding

2 

____

3 

____

4 

____

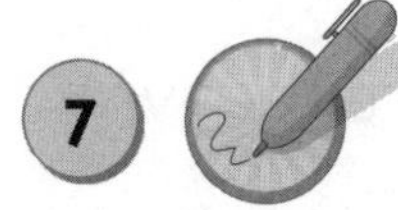

Look at Activity 6 and write.

1 He goes snowboarding in winter.

2 She ________ in ________.

3 He ________ in ________.

4 They ________ in ________.

Read and number.

1 She likes eating peaches in summer.

2 She goes to the park in winter.

3 She likes smelling the flowers in spring.

4 She likes flying her kite in autumn.

Read and write.

Look at this picture. This is me at the beach last summer. It was warm. I love going water skiing in summer.

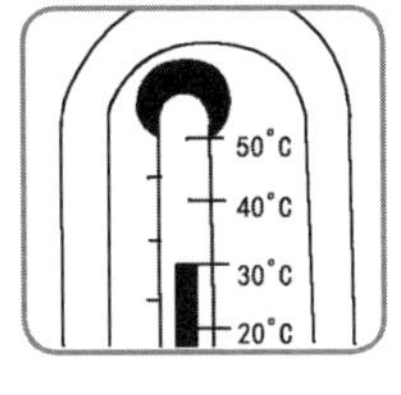

1 What was the weather like last summer?

It was warm.

2 What was the temperature?

____

3 What does she do in summer?

____

I like this picture. It's me skiing last winter. It was cold at the ski slope. I love skiing in winter.

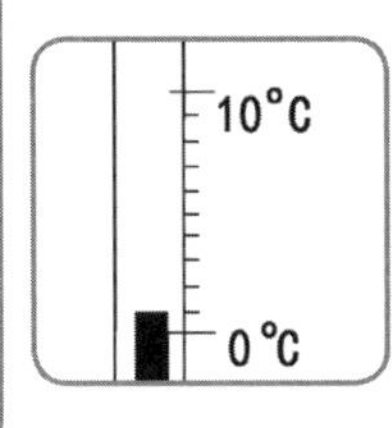

4 What was the weather like last winter?

____

5 What was the temperature?

____

6 What does he do in winter?

____

10  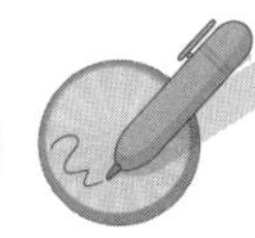 Write. Then number the pictures in order.

Hot milk. Thank you! And now it's snowy and cold! Where's Sophie?
Now there's thunder and lightning! ~~It's 38 degrees!~~ Ready? Action!

It's 38 degrees!

11 Look at Activity 10. Then read and write.

a What's the temperature? It's 38 degrees!
b Does Sophie like milk? ______
c Do they go camping? ______
d Is Sophie a snowman? ______
e Is it snowy and cold? ______
f Is it hot and sunny? ______

PHONICS

ew y

12 Read the words. Circle the pictures.

~~chew~~ fly new sky

13 Listen and connect the letters. Then write.

1:80

1	l	oi	k	______
2	c	ea	l	______
3	m	ee	f	leaf
4	w	ai	n	______

14 Listen and write the words.

1:81

1 stew 2 ______ 3 ______ 4 ______

15 Read aloud. Then listen and check.

1:82

In my new jet I fly up and down, high and low. I see the clouds and the sun, the rain and the snow. I like to be up in the sky.

16  Read and match.

1 

2 

a I like hot milk and toast for breakfast in winter.

b My summer holiday is in December and January.

c I live near a beautiful beach.

d I walk to school every day.

e We don't make snowmen here!

f The temperature is -2 degrees.

17  Read. Then write your answer.

1 Is winter cold and snowy in your country? ____________________

2 Is summer in December in your country? ____________________

3 Can you swim in spring in your country? ____________________

4 Do you make snowmen in winter in your country? ____________________

Read and circle.

HURRICANE QUIZ

1 The centre of the hurricane is
A the heart. **B** the eye.

2 In the centre of the hurricane
A it's windy. **B** it isn't windy.

3 There are hurricanes in the
A summer and autumn.
B winter and spring.

19 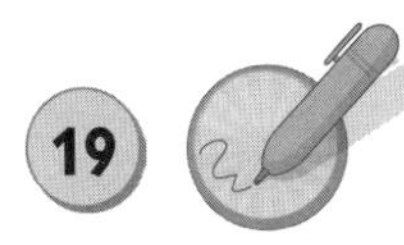

Write hurricane, typhoon or cyclone.

Korea
____

the United States
____

Australia
____

China
____

20 Look and write.

Across →

1 It's rainy. It's .

3 It's hot and .

5 The ____ today is 18°.

7 18° means 18 ____.

Down ↓

2 I can hear .

4 I can see .

6 It's . Let's go to the beach.

8 It's . We can't go to the beach.

21 Write.

goes skiing go snowboarding go water skiing
summer ~~winter~~ windy

Hi. It's [1] winter here and it's really cold. In winter I [2] ____________ with my friends. My sister [3] ____________. It's fun but I don' t like cold weather. I love hot weather and [4] ____________ is my favourite season! I [5] ____________ in summer when the water is warm. My sister loves summer, too. We don't like autumn because it's [6] ____________. What's your favourite season?

I CAN

I can identify weather, seasons and activities.
I can ask about the weather today and in the past.
I can understand a text about hurricanes.

ABOUT ME

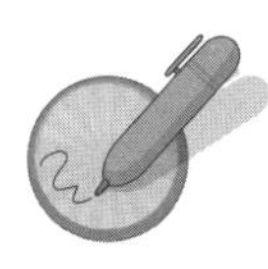

22 Think and write.

What was the weather like yesterday?

It ____.

23 Draw or stick a picture of your favourite season.

24 Write an email to your friend about your favourite season.

Hi, ______________. It's ______________ here and it's ______________.

____

____

____

____

____

____

4 My week

1 Match.

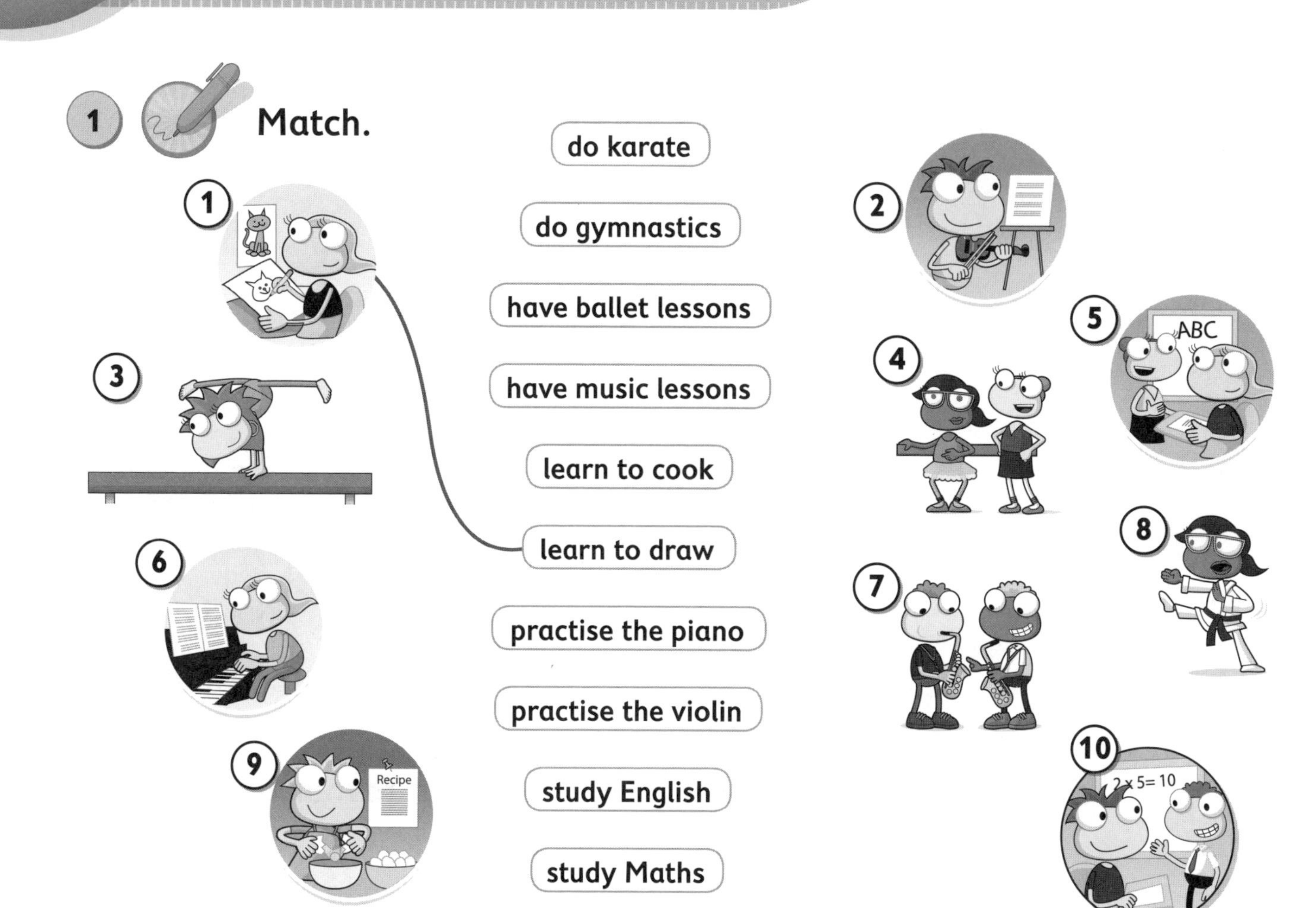

2 Write.

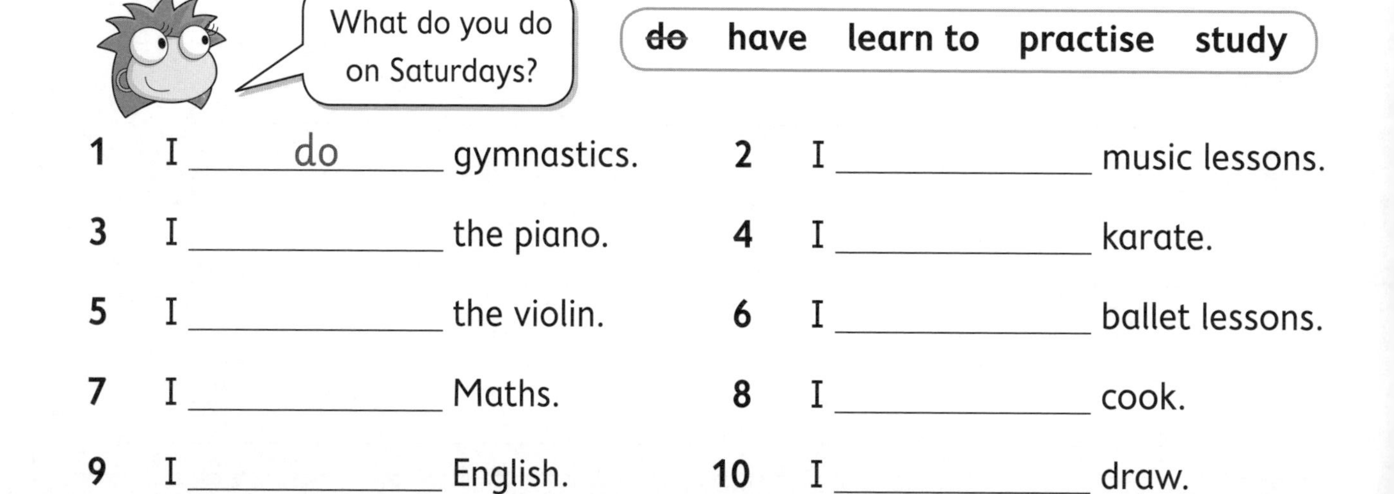

1 I ___do___ gymnastics.
2 I __________ music lessons.
3 I __________ the piano.
4 I __________ karate.
5 I __________ the violin.
6 I __________ ballet lessons.
7 I __________ Maths.
8 I __________ cook.
9 I __________ English.
10 I __________ draw.

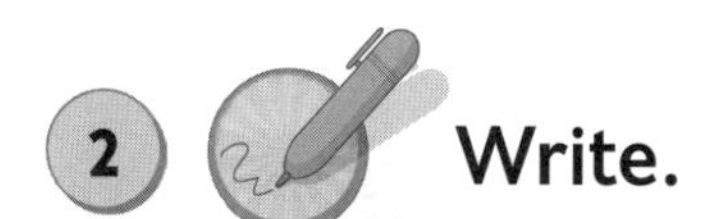

3 Look. Then read and write.

1 What does she do on Saturdays?

She has music lessons on Saturdays.

2 What does he do on Wednesdays?

____

3 ______________________________ Sundays?

____

4 ______________________________ Mondays?

____

5 ______________________________

____

4 Look at Activity 3 and write.

1 She has music lessons at 7 o'clock.

2 ______________________________

3 ______________________________

4 ______________________________

5 ______________________________

 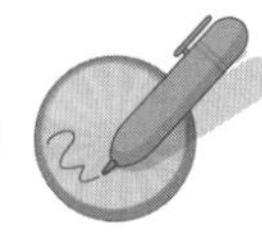

5 Look and write.

afternoon	quarter past 8	quarter to 9	
evening	half past 3	midday	~~morning~~

1 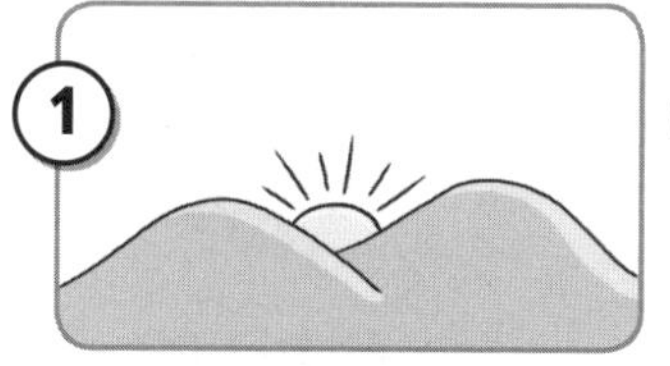

morning

2 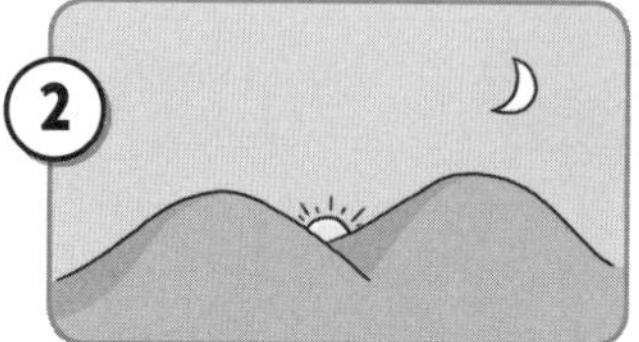

______

3 

______

4 

______

5 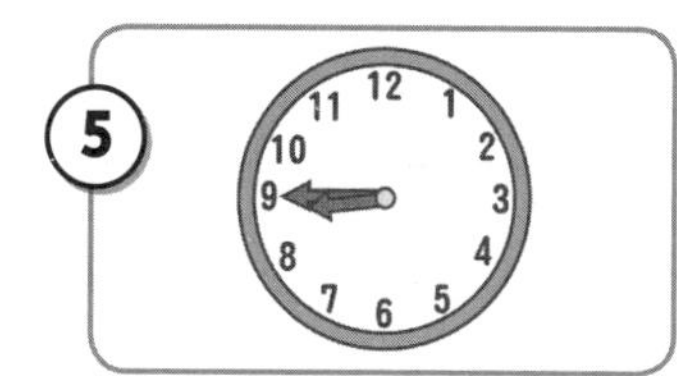

______

6 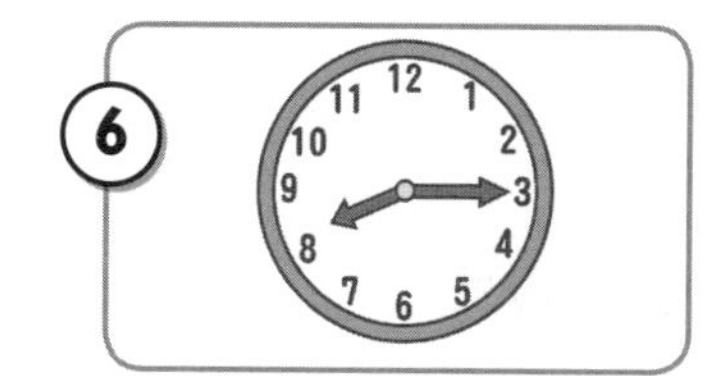

______

7 

______

6 Listen and match.

2:10

  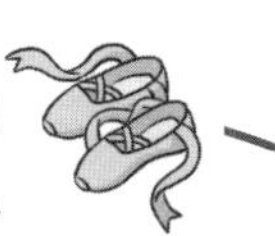

5 

e 

7 Listen and draw the time. Then write.

2:13

1 2 3 4

1 She goes swimming at 10 o'clock.

2 She ______ at ______.

3 She ______ at ______.

4 ______

8 Look. Then read and write.

1

When does she learn to cook?

She learns to cook in the morning.

2

When does he ______?

______

3

______?

______

4

______?

______

9 Write about you.

1 I always ______ (always)

2 ______ (often)

3 ______ (never)

10 Read. Then number the pictures in order.

11 Look at Activity 10. Then read and write.

1 When does Coco have music lessons? In the afternoon.

2 Does Coco have ballet lessons? ____________

3 Does he do karate? ____________

4 Can he jump and swing? ____________

5 Can he do gymnastics? ____________

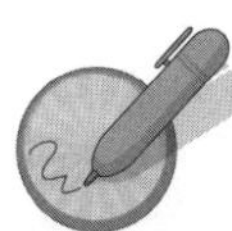

12 Write about Coco's activities.

____________ ____________ ____________

____________ ____________ ____________

PHONICS

ie ue

  Read the words. Circle the pictures.

~~glue~~ lie pie tie

14 2:18 Listen and connect the letters. Then write.

1	c	i	ke	cake
2	h	a	pe	______
3	d	a	me	______
4	sh	o	ve	______

15 2:19 Listen and write the words.

1 fried 2 ______ 3 ______ 4 ______

16 2:20 Read aloud. Then listen and check.

Ha-ha-ha! The man with the tie has got glue on his boots. He can't run.
He is stuck with the pie in his hand.

  **Read and write.**

My name is ____________. This is my timetable for ____________. My favourite subject is ____________.

I like break time. I play ____________ with my friends in the playground.
I have P.E., but then I have Art. Art isn't my ____________ subject. I eat a ____________ and ____________ for lunch on Tuesdays.

We have afternoon ____________ at 2.30. We sometimes sing songs.

Today after school, I've got chess club. It starts at ____________. I love it!

George's Tuesday timetable
Arrive: 8.50
Maths: 9.10 (favourite!)
English: 10.00
Break: 10.00 – 10.30 (football!)
P.E.: 10.30
Art: 11.15 (not my favourite!)
Lunch: 12.00 (burger and chips!)
Science: 1.00
Afternoon assembly: 2.30
School finishes: 3.00 (after-school chess club)

18 **Look at Activity 20. Then read and write.**

1 What time does George arrive at school? ____at 8.50____
2 What time does English start? ____________
3 What time does Maths start? ____________
4 How long is break time? ____________
5 What does George do after school on Tuesdays? ____________

Listen and write. Then number.

20 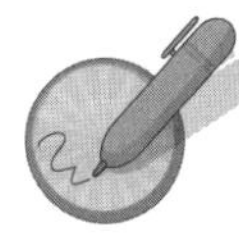

How do you and your friends go to school? Tick (✓) and write.

	By car	By bus	By bike	By boat	By train	Walk
1 Me						
2						
3						

1 I ______________________________.

2 ______________ goes ______________________.

3 ______________________________

21  Listen, number and tick (✓).

☐  ☐  ☐

1  ☐  ✓

☐ 

☐ 

☐

☐  ☐  ☐

22 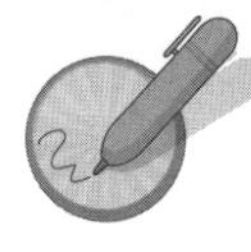 What does Julie do on Saturdays? Write.

9.15 – 10.00		
1.30 – 2.00		
2.45 – 3.30		
4.00 – 4.30		

I can identify scheduled activities and times of the day.
I can use *always*, *often* and *never*.
I can understand texts about how children go to school.

ABOUT ME

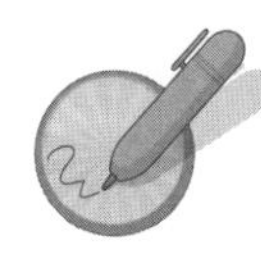

23 Write one activity and time for each day.

Sunday	Monday	Tuesday	Wednesday
Study Maths, afternoon			

Thursday	Friday	Saturday

24 Look at Activity 23. Write your own questions and answers.

1 What do you do on Sundays?

On Sundays I always study Maths in the afternoon.

2 ______________________________

On Wednesdays ______________________________.

3 ______________________________

On Fridays ______________________________.

4 ______________________________

On Saturdays ______________________________.

5 ______________________________

On Tuesdays ______________________________.

6 ______________________________

On Thursdays ______________________________.

5 Jobs

1 Look and write. a e i o u

1 f_i_r_e_f_i_ght_e_r 2 b__sk__tb__ll pl__y__r 3 b__ll__t d__nc__r

4 p__l__c__ __ff__c__r 5 b____ld__r 6 f__lm st__r 7 __str__n____t

2 Look and write.

3 Listen and number. 2:37

a  ☐ b  ☐ c  1 d 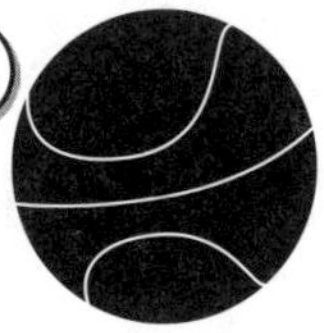 ☐

e 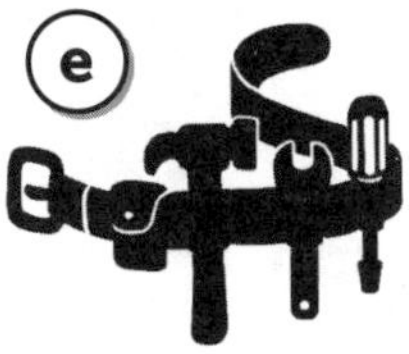 ☐ f  ☐ g ☐

4 Look at Activity 3 and write.

1 What does she want to be? She wants to be a police officer.

2 What does he want to be? ______________________

3 ________ does ________ want to be?

____

4 What does ______________________?

____

5 ______________________ want to be?

____

6 ______________________?

____

7 ______________________?

____

 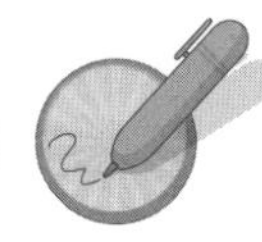

Look and write.

athlete carpenter ~~journalist~~ lawyer
mechanic model photographer singer

1 

journalist

2 

3 

4 

5 

6 

7 

8 

6 Unscramble and write.

1 he / want / does / to / a / be / singer (✗)

Does he want to be a singer?

No, he doesn't.

2 want / be / to / lawyer / does / a / she (✓)

3 a / do / want / be / to / you / fashion designer (✓)

4 computer programmer / he / want / does / to / a / be (✗)

7 Listen and tick (✓) or cross (✗).

2:42

1 a ✓ b ✗

2 a COURT b

3 a b

4 a b POLICE

8 Listen again. Then write.

2:43

1 He wants to be a journalist because he wants to ____________.
He doesn't want to be a ____________.

2 She ____________.
She ____________.

3 Why does she want to be ____________?
She ____________ because ____________.

4 Why ____________?
He ____________.

9 Write the questions. Then write your own answers.

1 Do you ____________? ______, I ______.

2 ____________
____

3 ____________
____

 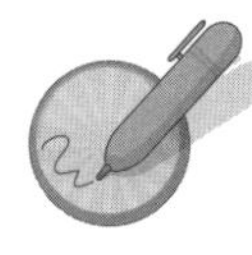

Look and write.

computers	taking pictures	space	helping people

1

He likes helping people.

He wants to be a ______.

2

She ______.

She ______.

3

______

______

4

______

______

11 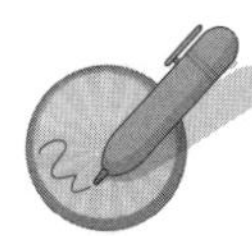

Look and write.

______

______

PHONICS
le y

  Read the words. Circle the pictures.

~~jungle~~ paddle rainy sunny

 13 Listen and connect the letters. Then write.

1	s	e	ll	ll	________
2	y	w	e	m	swim
3	s	c	i	f	________
4	s	m	ar	ow	________

 14 Listen and write the words.

1 little 2 ________ 3 ________ 4 ________

 15 Read aloud. Then listen and check.

We paddle down the river in our boat. The jungle is loud and the sun is hot. Look at that yellow snake! Look at that red and blue bird!

16 Read and write.

Natalia Osipova

Evie's blog

My name is Evie and I'm from Scotland. I love ballet dancing. I want to be a famous ballet dancer one day. Ballet dancers train a lot, so I have ballet lessons after school on Tuesdays and Fridays and on Saturday mornings, too. I love it! My hero is a Russian ballet dancer, Natalie Osipova. She is graceful and strong. I want to be as strong as her!

Evie, 10, Scotland

Alexander's blog

I'm Alexander. I'm from Germany. I like playing football. I want to be a famous football player one day. My favourite team is Bayern Munich. My favourite German footballer is Manuel Neuer. He's brilliant!

Alexander, 10, Germany

Manuel Neuer

1 Who wants to be a ballet dancer? ________________

2 Who wants to be a football player? ________________

17 Read and write *T* = *True* or *F* = *False*.

1 Evie likes ballet dancing. [T]

2 Alexander hasn't got a favourite football team. [ ]

3 Natalia Osipova is from Russia. [ ]

4 Manuel Neuer is a basketball player. [ ]

Listen and circle.

1

Hello, Matthew. What do you want to be and why?

I want to be a (/) player because I love sports.

2

What do you do to make your dreams come true?

I go running at (/) in the morning.

I eat only healthy food like (/). In the afternoon I practise (/) with the team.

3

What other things do you do?

I (/) on Sundays. I want to make my body strong.

Draw your dream job. Then write.

I want to be ______________________

because I ______________________

______________________.

____

____

I CAN DO IT!

20 Look and write the jobs.

1  police officer
2 ______ 
3 ______ 
4 ______ 
5 ______ 
6 ______ 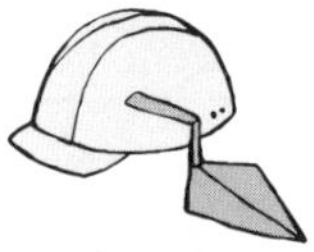
7 ______ 
8 ______

21 2:56 Listen, number and tick (✓). Then write.

COURT

[ ] a [ ] b [ ] 
[ ] a [ ] b [ ] 
[ ] a [ ] b [ ] 
[1] a [✓] b [ ]

1 Does he want to be a firefighter? Yes, he does.
2 ______ No, she doesn't.
3 What does she want to be? ______
4 What does he want to be? ______

I CAN

I can identify common jobs.
I can ask and answer about what people want to be and why.
I can understand texts about what other children want to be.

Draw and write two things you want to be and two things you don't want to be.

✓

I want to be ______ because ______ ______.	______ ______ ______

✗

I don't want to be ______.	______

6 In the rainforest

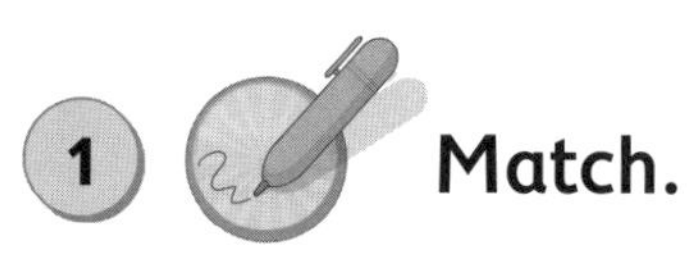

1 Match.

bridge | hut | mountain | nest | valley | vines | waterfall

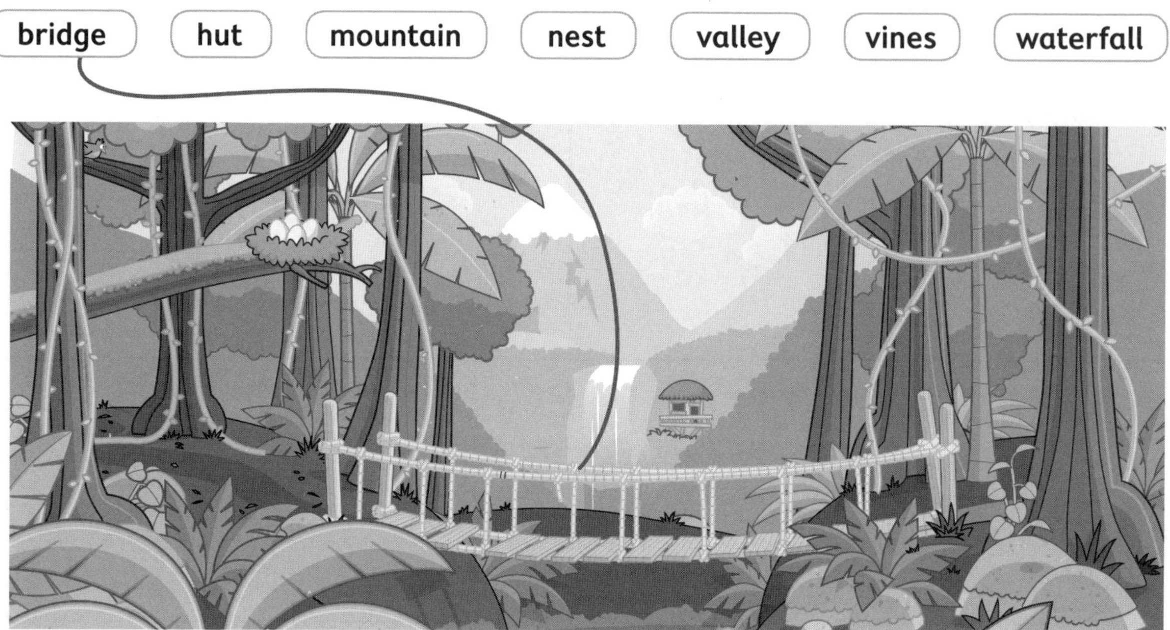

2 Look. Then read and write.

across	between ... and	near	over

1 I'm swimming ___across___ the ___river___.

2 The bird is flying ____________ the ____________.

3 She's standing ____________ the ____________.

4 The ____________ is ____________ the lake ______ the trees.

 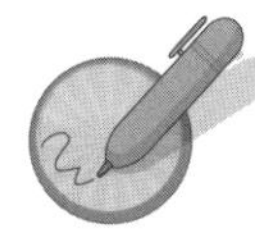

Look. Then read and write.

1 Where's the doctor? She's near the vines.

2 ____________ giraffe? It's ____________.

3 ____________ bus? It's ____________.

4 ____________ ____________

Listen and number. Then write.

Where are the elephants?

They're over the mountain

____________.

____

____

____

____

____

____

____

____

____

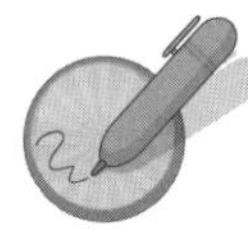

5 Unscramble and write. Then match.

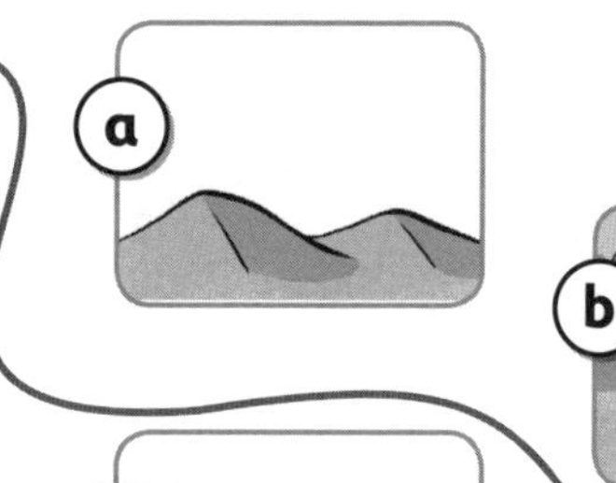

1 akle lake

2 eas ____________

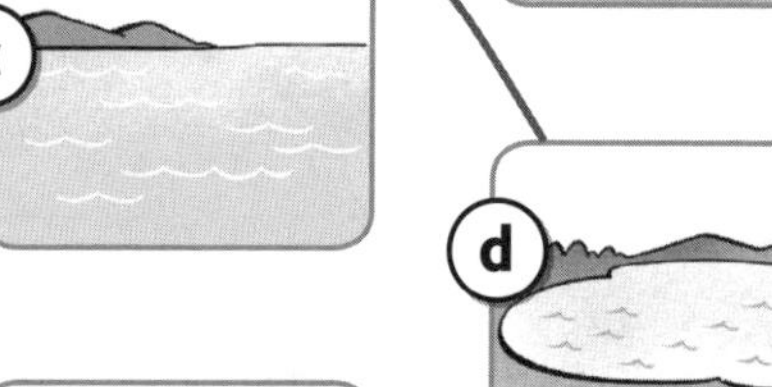

3 slihl ____________

4 staco ____________

5 stap ____________

6 rowdats ____________

7 orthhug ____________

8 donuar ____________

6 Read and tick (✓).

1 They couldn't go towards the hills.

2 He could swim across the river.

3 She couldn't walk past the lake.

4 He could walk around the mountain.

  **Listen and write ✓ = could or ✗ = couldn't. Then write.**

1 We couldn't go by bus but we could go by plane.

2 We ____________ swim ____________ the lake.

3 The huts were ____________ the ____________.

4 We couldn't go near the lions but we ____________ walk ____________ them.

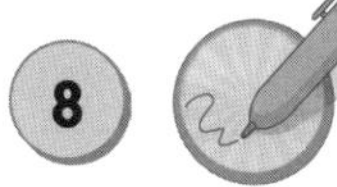 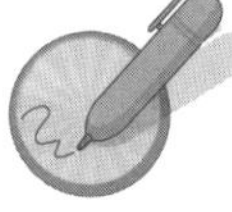 **Write.**

climb	play	stay	walk

1 I walked in the rainforest yesterday.

2 We ____________ in a hut last summer.

3 I ____________ a tree last Saturday.

4 They ____________ football at school last week.

9  Read. Then number the pictures in order.

10 Look at Activity 9. Read and match.

1 First the man gives the map to Sophie.

2 First they run across the bridge.

3 First Oliver thinks it is a rope.

4 First they fall into the lake.

a Then they swing through the waterfall.

b Then they follow Oliver.

c Then Sophie says it's a snake.

d Then they find the cave.

11 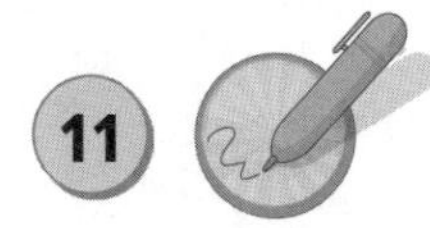 Choose a picture from Activity 9 and write.

I like Picture f . Sophie's with the snake. I like this picture because it's very funny.

I like Picture ____. ______________________________

____

12 Read the words. Circle the pictures.

~~circle~~ circus ice princess

13 Listen and connect the letters. Then write.

1	f	e	a	p	______
2	g	l	tt	ss	______
3	l	l	a	g	flag
4	s	l	ee	er	______

14 Listen and write the words.

1 centre 2 ______ 3 ______ 4 ______

15 Read aloud. Then listen and check.

The princess is at home and the circus is here. It's a sunny day and the circus is funny but the princess isn't happy. She wants to go to the city.

  **Look. Then read and write.**

butterflies and snakes | the UK | bald eagle | Sherwood Forest | Six Rivers National Forest | horse riding | the United States | ~~camping~~

1

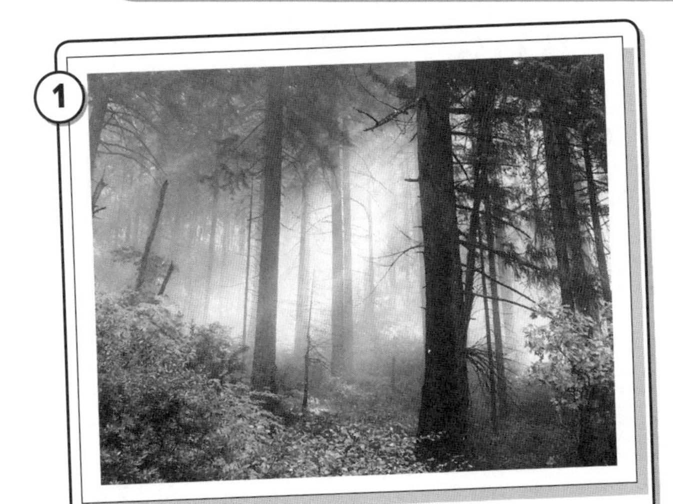

Name of forest: ______________________

____

Country: ______________________

Animals: ______________________

Activities: camping

2

Name of forest: ______________________

____

Country: ______________________

Animals: ______________________

Activities: ______________________

17 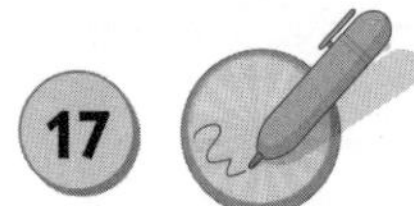 **Look at Activity 16. Then read and write.**

1 This is ______________ Forest.
It's in ______________.
There are tall trees and grass there.

2 This is ______________ Forest.
It's in ______________.
There's a ______________ in this forest.

  **Read and write.**

giant tarantula   hummingbird   parrot   ~~tapir~~

1 I've got a short neck. I live near the river. I eat bananas. What animal am I?

tapir

2 I can fly. I've got a long tail and colourful feathers. What animal am I?

____

3 I can fly. I'm very small. I like flowers. What animal am I?

____

4 I'm a big spider. I've got long legs. I'm scary. What animal am I?

____

19 **Write about your favourite rainforest animal.**

My favourite rainforest animal is the piranha. Piranhas are a kind of fish. They've got very sharp teeth. They live in the Amazon River. They eat meat, fruit and seeds. I like them because they're scary.

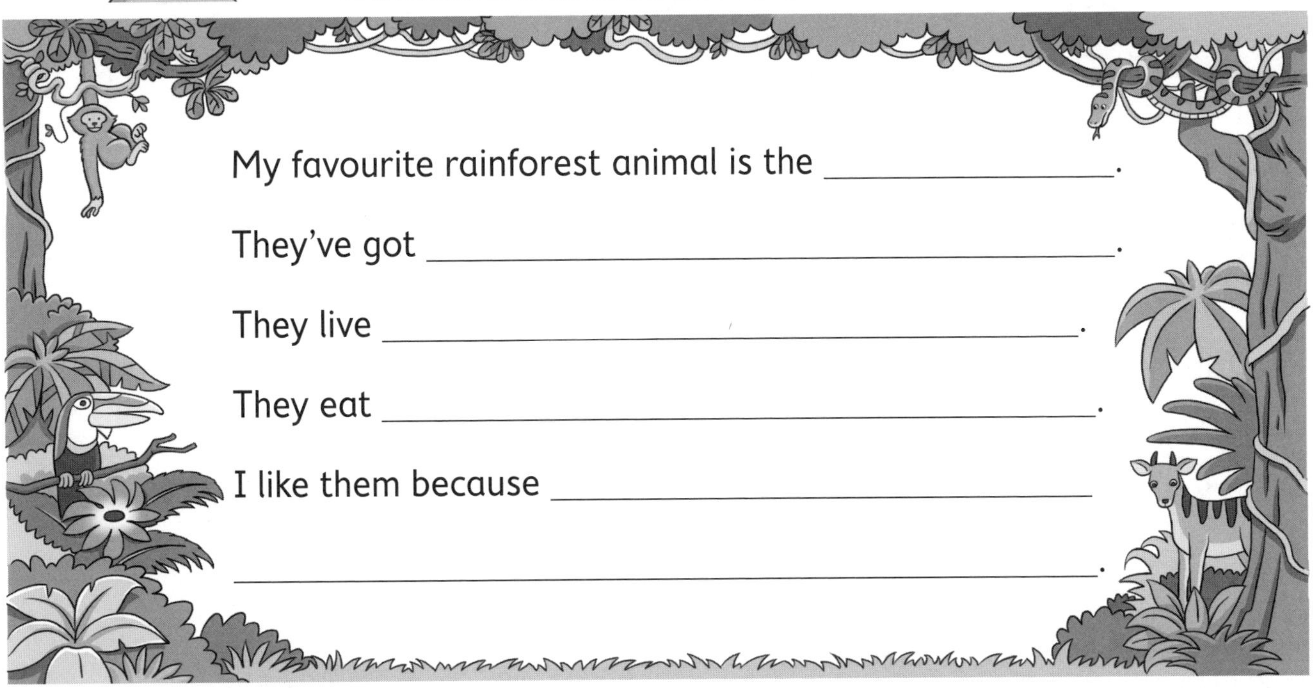

My favourite rainforest animal is the ________________.

They've got ________________________________.

They live ________________________________.

They eat ________________________________.

I like them because ____________________________

____.

I CAN DO IT!

20 Look and write.

Across ➡

1 The boat is moving towards the ___.

3 I want to swim in the ___.

5 He walked past the ___.

7 The monkeys are on the ___.

Down ⬇

2 A ___ looks like a house.

4 A ___ is taller than a hill.

6 A baby bird lives in a ___.

8 People use a ___ to get from one side to the other.

1 C O A S T

21 Look. Then read, write and answer.

Yesterday the monkeys (play) ________________ on the vines. Then they (look) ________________ at the mountain. Then they (climb) ________________ over the mountain. Then I couldn't see the monkeys. Do you know where they are?

I CAN

I can talk about the rainforest and use prepositions.
I can write about the past.
I can understand a text about the Amazon rainforest.

Look. Then read and write.

1 Where's the river?
It's between the elephants and the lions.

2 ______________________
They're near the hills.

3 Is the lake next to the river?
____

4 Is the waterfall near the bridge?
____

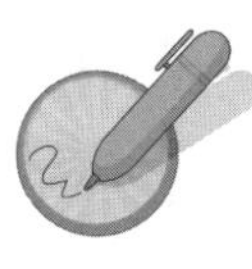

Imagine you were on the island in Activity 22. Write about what you could and couldn't do.

1 I could ______________________.

2 I couldn't ______________________.

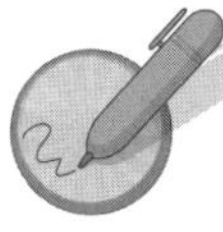

Look and write. Then draw and write about you.

1 He walked through the forest yesterday.

2 She ______________________ last week.

3 I ______________________.

7 Feelings

 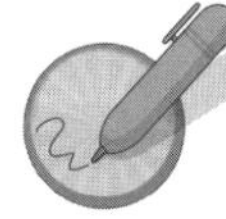 Look and write.

blushing	crying	frowning	~~laughing~~
shaking	shouting	smiling	yawning

He's laughing.

2 

She's ____________.

3 

She's ____________.

4 

He's ____________.

He's ____________.

6 

He's ____________.

7 

She's ____________.

8 

She's ____________.

  Draw the correct faces.

1 The police officer is angry.
She's shouting.

2 The builder is tired.
He's yawning.

3 The film star is sad.
She's crying.

4 The firefighter is happy.
He's smiling.

  Listen and number.

4 Look at Activity 3 and write.

1 he / shouting / angry — Why is he shouting? He's shouting because he's angry.

2 you / yawning / tired — Why are you ____________? I'm ____________ because I'm ____________.

3 she / smiling / happy ____________________________________

____

4 she / crying / sad ____________________________________

____

5 he / frowning / bored ____________________________________

____

6 you / laughing / excited ____________________________________

____

 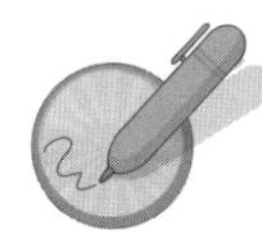

5 Look and write.

embarrassed nervous proud relaxed relieved surprised ~~worried~~

1 

worried

2 

______

3 

______

4 

______

5 

______

6 

______

7 

______

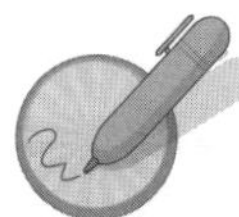

6 Look and write.

1 What's the matter?

I'm embarrassed.

2 How do you feel?

I feel ______.

3 What's the matter?

______

4 How do you feel?

______

7 Listen and tick (✓).

3:13

1 sad a ✓ b

2 nervous a b

3 worried a b

4 scared a b

8 Look at Activity 7 and write.

being sick	crocodiles	flying	rainy days
running	singing	snakes	swimming

1 What makes you feel sad? Rainy days make me feel sad.

2 What makes ________?

________ makes me feel ________.

3 What ________?

________ makes ________.

4 ________?

________ make ________.

9 Match and write.

1 He's worried.

2 I can't do this activity.

3 It's her birthday.

4 Get the books.

a Send ________ a present.

b Give him a hug.

c Put ________ on the shelf.

d Can you help ________?

Look. Then read and write.

~~dinosaurs~~ relieved scared worried

1 What makes Oliver feel nervous?

dinosaurs

2 What's the matter?

____

3 How does Oliver feel?

____

4 How does Oliver feel now?

____

 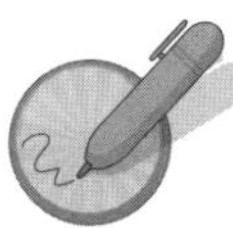

Write about the dinosaur.

Is it big? Does it have a long tail? Does it have sharp claws?

The dinosaur ______________________

____

______________________.

 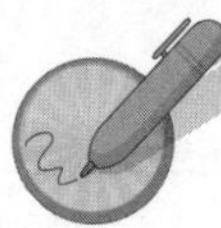

Find out about a real dinosaur. Then write.

1 Name: ______________________

2 Food: ______________________

3 Special body parts: ______________________

  **Read the words. Circle the pictures.**

14  **Listen and connect the letters. Then write.**

1	g	l	ee	n	green
2	c	r	ou	n	______
3	t	p	oo	n	______
4	s	r	ai	d	______

15 3:19 **Listen and write the words.**

1 edge 2 ______ 3 ______ 4 ______

16  **Read aloud. Then listen and check.**

The gentleman looks at the gems. There are lots of small gems but he likes the large gem. 'How much is it?' he asks. Now he sighs, the price is too high.

17 Read and match.

1 Victoria's blog

Hi! I'm Victoria. I go to a special music school. At school we have singing and dancing lessons every day. We go by bus and train to other schools and sing in concerts. Singing makes me feel happy because I love music.

Victoria, 10, South Africa

2 Mark's blog

My name's Mark. I'm from Canada. Every year we have a festival called Winter Carnival. It makes me feel happy because it's fun. I go to Carnival with my family. We go skating, eat pancakes and drink hot chocolate. In the photo we're wearing beanies and scarves because it's cold.

Mark, 10, Canada

a 

b 

18 Read and write.

1 How does Victoria go to other schools?

She goes by bus and train.

2 Why does Victoria like singing?

____

3 What makes Mark feel happy?

____

4 What do they do at Winter Carnival?

____

19 

Read. Then listen and circle.

1 I'm (crying / laughing) because it's funny.

2 I'm (relieved / worried).

3 It makes me feel (scared / relaxed).

4 I feel (nervous / surprised) and happy.

20 Write the name of a song, singer or band.

1 What music makes you feel happy?

____

2 What music makes you feel relaxed?

____

3 What music makes you feel excited?

____

4 What music makes you feel sad?

____

 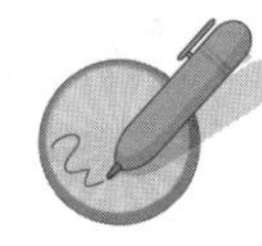

Look and write.

frowning	laughing	nervous	relaxed
relieved	scared	shouting	smiling

She's smiling because she's relieved.

____

____

____

22 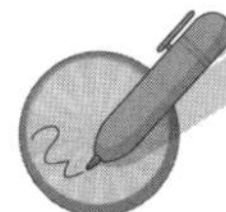

Write.

1 She likes flowers. Buy her some for her birthday.

2 Can you help ________? They're worried about the test.

3 Can you make ________ lunch, please. We're hungry.

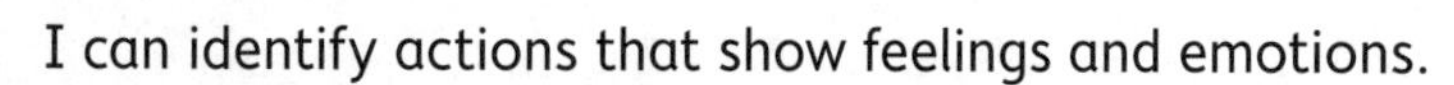

I CAN

I can identify actions that show feelings and emotions.
I can use *me*, *him*, *her*, *it*, *them* and *us*.
I can understand how music and films make me feel.

7

23 Write.

angry bored happy ~~sad~~
nervous proud hurt tired

crying	smiling	yawning	shaking
sad			

24 Look. Then read and circle.

My name's Mario. In this picture I'm [1] (smiling / frowning) because I'm excited and [2] (sad / happy). My [3] (football / basketball) team is this year's champion. Winning a game [4] (make / makes) me feel [5] (proud / embarrassed).

25 Draw or stick a picture of yourself. Then write.

My name's

_______________.

In this picture I'm

____

____

____

_______________.

8 By the sea

1 Match.

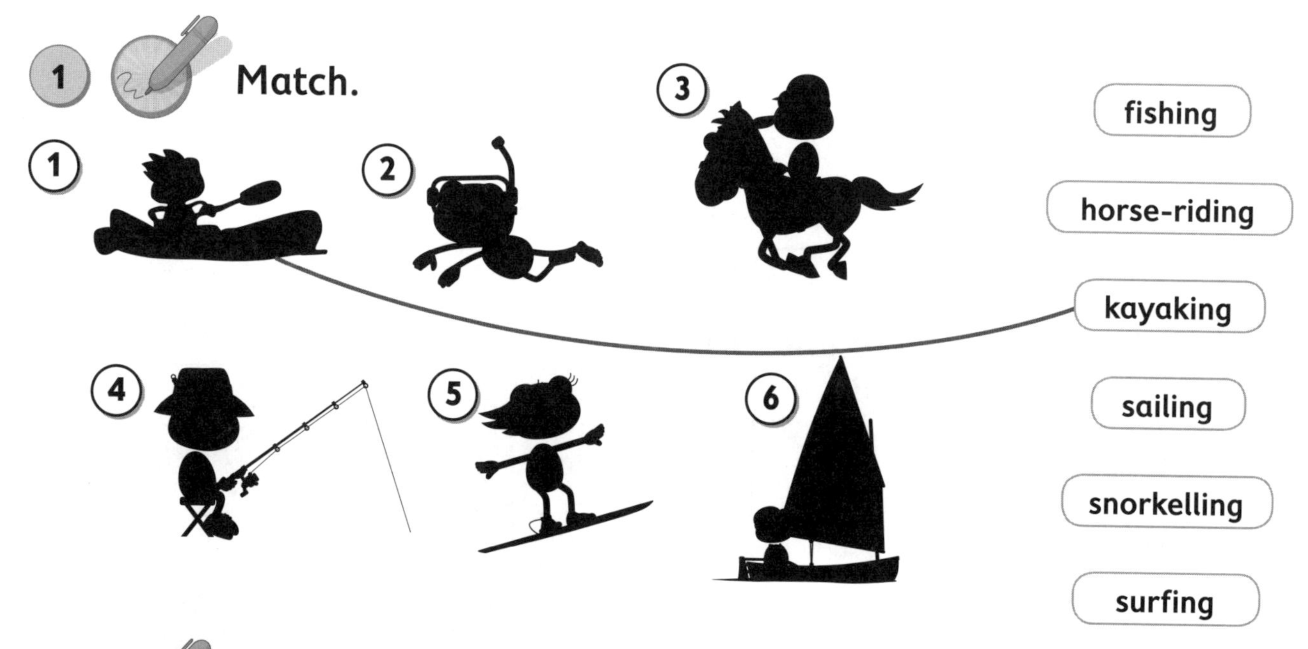

2 Unscramble the words. Then look and write.

farsorbud file takecj ~~ginfshi ord~~ grinid stoob norelsk peldad

1 Joe is fishing.
He has a fishing rod.

2 Oliver is ______.
He has a ______.

3 Sophie is on a ______. She loves ______.

4 Coco is ______. He's wearing ______.

5 Finley Keen is sailing, but he isn't wearing a ______.

6 Jane is kayaking, but she doesn't have a ______.

3 

Listen, number and tick (✓).

4 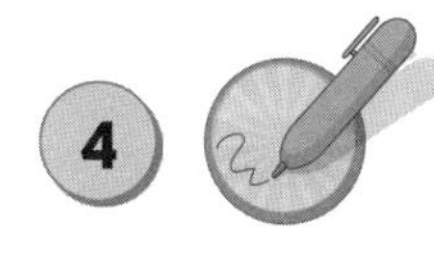

Look and write.

1 

Let's go horse-riding!

Great idea! I love horse-riding.

2 

______________________________!

Sorry, I don't like ______________________.

3 

____

____

4 

____

____

Have you got ______________________?

Yes, I have.

 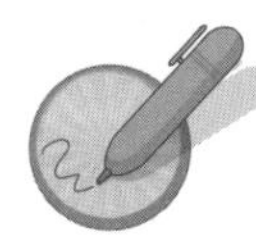

Look and write.

bungee jumping | scuba diving | ~~hang gliding~~ | rafting | rock climbing

1 

hang gliding

2 

____

3 

____

4 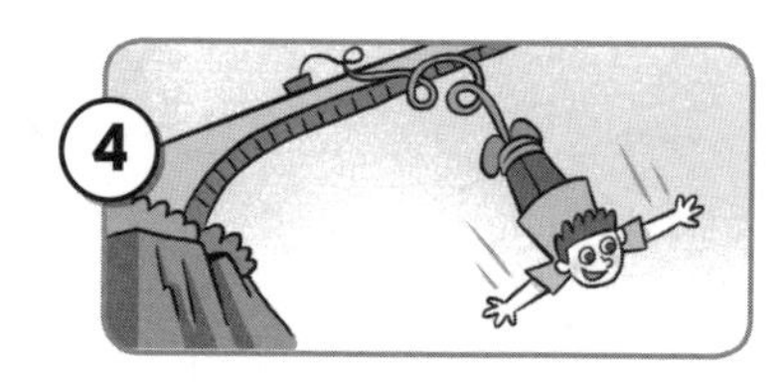

____

5 

____

6 Write. Then listen and match.

3:36

bored with | ~~crazy about~~ | fond of | scared of | terrified of

1 crazy about

  ______________________

  ______________________

  ______________________

  ______________________

7 Look at Activity 6 and write.

1 What's she crazy about? She's crazy about scuba diving.

2 What's ______? ______

3 ______ ______

4 ______ ______

5 ______ ______

8 Look and write.

1 What are you going to do? I'm going to go sailing.

2 ______ they ______? ______

3 ______ she ______? ______

9 Write about yourself. Then draw or stick a picture.

What are you terrified of? I'm terrified of ______ ______.	What are you going to do tomorrow? I'm ______ ______.

10  **Read. Then number the pictures in order.**

11 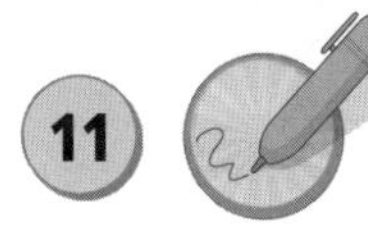 **Write.**

bananas fond of horse-riding
knows making monkey ~~film star~~

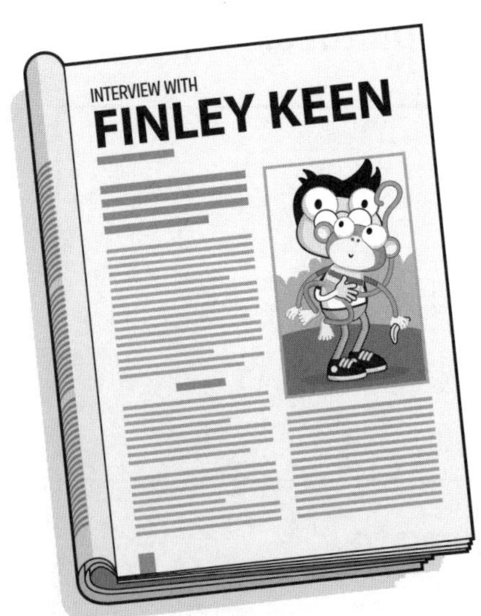

Finley Keen is a famous [1] film star. He's crazy about [2] __________ films. He is also very [3] __________ sailing. His new film is *Return to Banana Valley.*

His best friend is Coco. Coco is a very clever [4] __________. Coco wants to be a film star like Finley Keen. He [5] __________ all the words in the new film. Coco says, 'My favourite food is [6] __________, and I'm fond of [7] __________.'

12 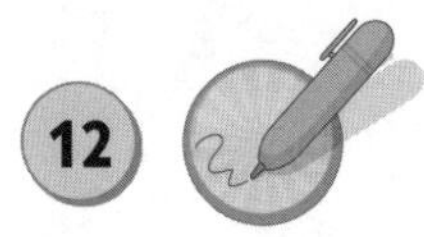 **Look at Activity 11 and write.**

1 What is Finley Keen crazy about? __________

2 What is Coco fond of? __________

PHONICS

ph **wh**

  **Read the words. Circle the pictures.**

~~dolphin~~ phone whale whisper

14 **Listen and connect the letters. Then write.**

3:43

1	p	i	n	y	______
2	b	u	nn	p	______
3	t	u	m	le	______
4	f	ai	ck	t	paint

15 **Listen and write the words.**

3:44

1 elephant 2 ______ 3 ______ 4 ______

16 **Read aloud. Then listen and check.**

3:45

Look, the whale and the dolphin are on the phone! Here comes the shark. The fish are whispering. What's that on his head? Oh, it's a funny hat!

 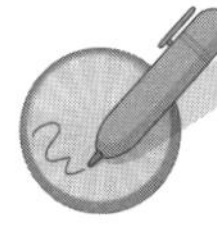 **Look and write.**

rafting ~~horse-riding~~ beach volleyball kayaking surfing snorkelling

1 
horse-riding

2 
____

3 
____

4 
____

5 
____

6 
____

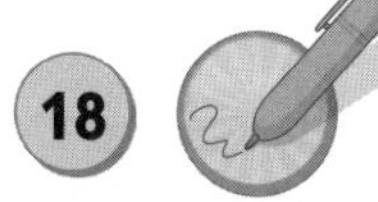 **Plan a summer camp. Then write.**

Monday	Tuesday	Wednesday
go rafting		

1 On Monday we're going to go rafting, ________ and ________.

2 On Tuesday ____________________.

3 ____________________

19 Look and write.

colourful fish hot ~~rainforests~~ sea sea animals white

1 Coral reefs are called the rainforests of the sea.

2 There are a lot of ________ and ________ on coral reefs.

3 Coral reefs are ________.

4 Some coral reefs die when the ________ becomes too ________.

5 The colour of dead coral reef is ________.

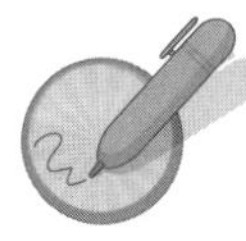

20 Look and write.

~~butterfly~~ butterfly fish seahorse lion parrot parrotfish sea snake horse snake starfish

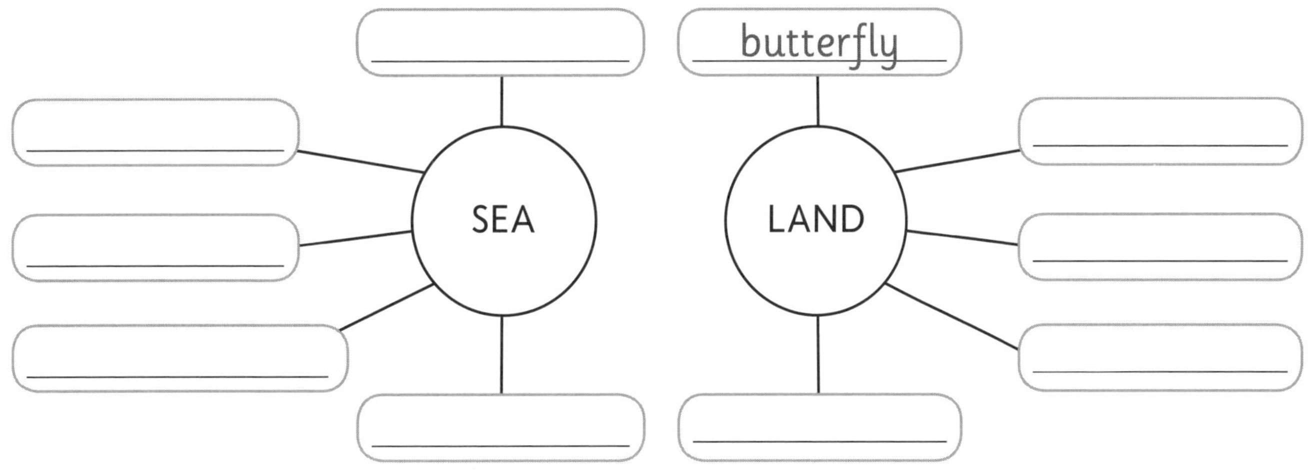

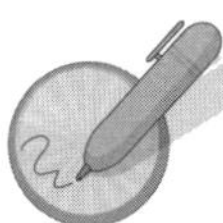

21 Think and write.

Why are most coral reefs found in warm seas?

____

 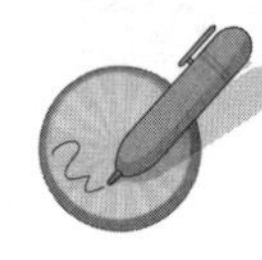 **Look and write.**

1. **A:** Let's go sailing! Have you got a life jacket?
   B: No, I haven't.

2. **A:** ______________________
   Have ______________________?
   B: Yes, ______________________.

3. **A:** ______________________
   B: Great idea. I love ______________________.
   I like watching the fish.

4. **A:** What are you going to do next week?
   B: I'm ______________________
   ______________________.

5. **A:** What are ______________________?
   B: I'm ______________________
   ______________________.

I can identify outdoor activities, sports and equipment.
I can talk about what I'm going to do.
I can understand a text about coral reefs.

  **Look. Then read and write.**

Hi, Gerry,

I'm having a great time here. In the morning I go

1 horse-riding. I'm fond of it. It makes me feel relaxed. In the evening we go 2 ______. But I'm

3 ______ it. I don't like it very much. We're going to go 4 ______ on Saturday. I'm

5 ______ it. It makes me feel proud that I can do it.

Tomorrow I'm going to go 6 ______.

Raphael

24 **Pretend you are on holiday. Write an email to a friend.**

1 Look. Then read and write.

1 What's his name? ____________________

2 What ____________________? He likes making films and watching TV.

3 Why ____________________? He's smiling because he's happy.

2 Listen and circle.

1 (a) riding a scooter (b) skateboarding (c) skiing

2 (a) (b) (c)

3 (a) Coco (b) Sophie (c) Oliver

4 (a) English (b) Maths (c) music

5 (a)  (b)  (c) 

6 (a) Sophie (b) Uncle James (c) Oliver

7 (a) surprised (b) scared (c) relaxed

8 (a)  (b)  (c) 

3 Look and write.

1 Who's your favourite character in the story?

My favourite character is ________________________
____.

2 What's your favourite chant about?

My favourite chant is about ________________________
____.

3 What's your favourite song about?

____
____

4 Think of your favourite film star. Stick a picture of him/her in a scene from a film. Then write.

My favourite film star is ________________________.

This scene is from the film ________________________.

In this scene he/she is ________________________. I like this scene because it makes me feel ________________________.

Listen and read about Willie. Then write about yourself.

My name is Willie. I'm 10 years old. I like playing the guitar and surfing the internet in my free time. I don't like painting or drawing. My favourite wild animal is the gorilla. Gorillas live in the rainforest and they eat leaves and fruit.

My name is ____

____

____

____.

6 

Look. Then read and write.

April. 5, Monday.	April. 6, Tuesday.	April. 7, Wednesday.	April. 8, Thursday.	April. 9, Friday.
19°C	20°C	25°C	20°C	19°C

1 It's Tuesday. What's the weather like today? It's ____wet____.

2 It's Friday. What's the temperature today? It's ____________.

3 It's Thursday. Is it humid? ____________, it ____________.

4 It's Wednesday. Is it stormy? ____________

5 It's Monday. Is it wet? ____________

  **Listen and read about Judy. Then write about yourself.**

My name is Judy. I'm 11 years old. I study hard every day. I play basketball with my friends on Wednesdays. I learn to cook with my grandmother on Saturdays. When I grow up I want to be a lawyer or a journalist.

My name is ______________________________

____

____

______________________________________.

8 **Look at the Pupil's Book. Read. Then write or draw the answers.**

1 What's a way of talking that is not the telephone? chatting online

2 What animal lives in rivers and eats meat and fish? ______________

3 What weather has thunder and lightning? ______________

4 What time is between morning and afternoon? ______________

5 What do you call a person who takes photos? ______________

6 What do you call the place where baby birds live? ______________

7 How do people feel if they do well at something? ______________

8 What do you need to go fishing? ______________

1 Find, circle and write the Halloween words.

1 moon

2 ________________

3 ________________

4 ________________

5 ________________

N	O	S	S	M	Y	S	E	S	S
M	L	N	S	O	R	L	O	S	M
M	E	M	E	E	M	E	L	N	M
T	A	O	N	F	W	N	O	N	K
Y	S	N	E	E	E	N	M	E	E
S	N	S	T	R	L	L	O	E	N
M	O	T	O	O	W	R	O	W	L
S	K	E	L	E	T	O	N	O	O
T	O	R	T	O	O	N	L	R	O
W	O	L	B	O	N	E	N	N	S

2 Look. Then read and write.

1 The children have got bags of sweets.

2 There are ________ owls.

3 The ________________ has got many bones.

4 The witch is on a ________________.

5 The children are ghosts and ________________.

1 Find, circle and write the Christmas words.

1 lunch
2 ____________
3 ____________
4 ____________
5 ____________
6 ____________
7 ____________

N	E	L	P	L	I	L	P	R	L
S	C	R	A	C	K	E	R	N	G
S	L	B	H	E	H	N	E	M	S
N	L	U	N	C	H	P	S	L	N
O	R	S	P	I	C	T	E	I	O
W	N	P	U	D	D	I	N	G	W
M	P	R	E	S	E	N	T	H	B
A	P	W	H	R	N	T	R	T	A
N	R	K	N	R	C	N	H	S	L
N	C	T	K	L	I	W	G	U	L

2 Look and write.

songs presents ~~lights~~ snowman turkey pudding snowballs

At Christmas we decorate a Christmas tree with [1] lights. We open and play with our [2] ____________. Then we cook a lunch with [3] ____________ and Christmas [4] ____________. When it's snowy we play with [5] ____________ and make a [6] ____________. In the evening we sing Christmas [7] ____________.

Mother's Day

1 Match.

toast

tea

box of chocolates

rose

Mum

present

2 Read. Then write your own note and draw a picture.

Dear Mum,
Happy Mother's Day!
You are my best friend.
I love you,
John

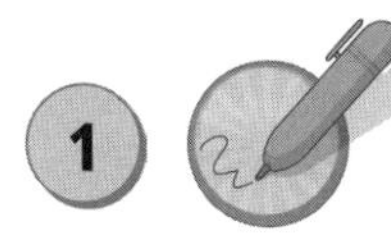

1 Match the words with the pictures.

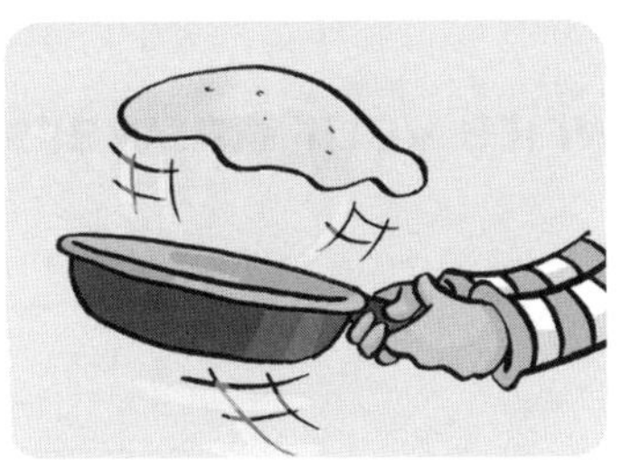

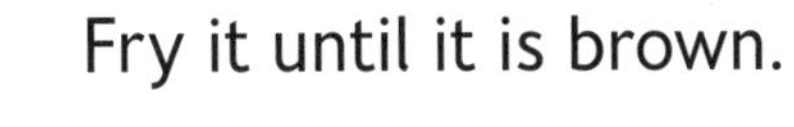

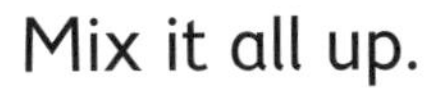

Fry it until it is brown.

Mix it all up.

Toss the pancake.

Pour the mixture.

Catch it if you can.

Add the eggs, milk and flour.

2 Think of a special day. Talk with your partner about special food, special clothes or special games. Draw a picture of your favourite day.

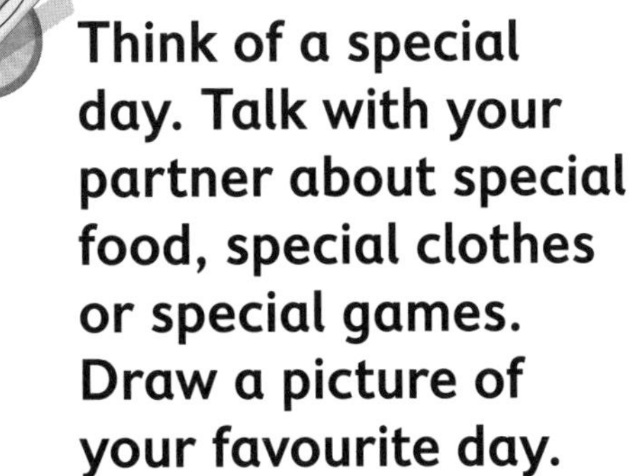

Welcome and Unit 1

1 Read. Then write your answers.

1 What's your name? ____________________

2 How old are you? ____________________

3 How old is your friend? ____________________

4 Is your friend older than you? ____________________

5 What's his/her favourite colour? ____________________

2 Complete the sentences.

1 Peter is taller than (tall) Cindy.

2 The cat is ____________ (small) the dog.

3 My hands are ____________ (big) my sister's hands.

4 Kim is ____________ (young) Paul.

5 My dad is ____________ (old) me.

3 Ask a friend the questions. Then write the answers.

1 What do you like doing? ____________________

2 Do you like skiing? ____________________

3 What does your mum like doing? ____________________

4 Do you like cooking? ____________________

Unit 2

1 Find, circle and write animal words.

O	H	C	A	M	E	L	G	Z
H	I	C	O	N	L	N	O	G
E	P	F	Z	N	E	B	R	I
L	P	P	A	N	D	A	I	R
R	O	C	A	E	M	E	L	A
H	L	G	O	F	Y	M	L	F
L	I	O	N	L	A	Z	A	F
C	R	O	C	O	D	I	L	E
E	L	E	P	H	A	N	T	R

1 gorilla
2 ____________
3 ____________
4 ____________
5 ____________
6 ____________
7 ____________
8 ____________

2 Write about the animals.

forests ~~grass~~ rivers meat leaves deserts

1 Zebras eat grass.
2 Hippos live in ____________.
3 Giraffes eat ____________.
4 Camels live in ____________.
5 Lions eat ____________.
6 Pandas live in ____________.

3 Read. Then write the answers.

1 Do lions eat leaves? No, they don't.
2 Do monkeys eat fruit? ____________
3 Where do gorillas live? ____________
4 Where do elephants live? ____________
5 What do gorillas eat? ____________

4 Match.

1 Crocodiles can swim
2 Crocodiles can't run
3 Crocodiles have got
4 Crocodiles eat
5 Crocodiles live

a fast.
b a lot of teeth.
c in rivers.
d meat and fish.
e very well.

Unit 3

1 **Read. Then write your answers.**

1 What's the weather like today? ____________________

2 What's the temperature today? ____________________

3 Is it warm? ____________________

4 Is it stormy? ____________________

2 **Write about what you and your partner do in each season.**

1 In spring, I ____________________. He/She ____________________.

2 In summer, I ____________________. He/She ____________________.

3 In autumn, I ____________________. He/She ____________________.

4 In winter, I ____________________. He/She ____________________.

3 **Draw and write about the weather.**

yesterday

last winter

1 ____________________ 2 ____________________

4 **Write about your favourite season.**

My favourite season is ______________. The weather is ______________

and ______________. In ______________ I like ______________.

Unit 4

1 **Write *do* or *have*.**

1 ____have____ music lessons
2 ____________ karate
3 ____________ gymnastics
4 ____________ ballet lessons

2 **Write *practise* or *learn to*.**

1 ____practise____ the violin
2 ____________ draw
3 ____________ cook
4 ____________ the piano

3 **Write about your week.**

1 What do you do on Mondays? ____________
2 What do you do on Saturdays? ____________
3 When do you study English? ____________
4 When do you study Maths? ____________

4 **Ask your friend about his/her week. Then write the answers.**

1 What does he/she do on Mondays? ____________
2 What does he/she do on Saturdays? ____________
3 When does he/she study English? ____________
4 When does he/she study Maths? ____________

5 **Write about yourself.** always often never

1 ____________
2 ____________
3 ____________

Unit 5

1 **Write the words in alphabetical order.**

singer journalist mechanic lawyer
firefighter builder
carpenter photographer ~~astronaut~~

1 astronaut 2 ______ 3 ______
4 ______ 5 ______ 6 ______
7 ______ 8 ______ 9 ______

2 **Ask a friend. Then write what you want and don't want to be.**

want to be

1 I ______ because ______.

2 He/She ______ because ______.

don't want to be

1 I ______.

2 He/She ______.

3 **Read. Then look at the answers and write.**

1 Do you want to be a farmer? No, I don't. (✗)

2 Does he want to be a journalist? ______ (✓)

3 What does she want to be? ______ (model)

4 ______ No, I don't want to be an athlete.

5 ______ He wants to be a lawyer.

4 **Write about your dream job.**

I want to be ______ because ______

______.

Unit 6

1 Find, circle and write nature words.

L	G	I	O	T	C	R	E	R
O	L	B	V	N	S	B	E	L
E	C	R	I	V	E	R	U	H
M	O	U	N	T	A	I	N	I
L	A	K	E	R	P	D	A	L
N	S	S	I	L	S	G	V	L
S	T	I	N	H	M	T	N	N
O	L	I	D	I	T	S	R	N
E	H	U	T	O	S	T	U	U

1 river ____ 2 ________

3 ________ 4 ________

5 ________ 6 ________

7 ________ 8 ________

2 Read and draw.

1 The river is between the hut and the mountain.

2 The monkey is near the hut.

3 The crocodile is in the river.

4 The birds are over the mountain.

3 Describe what you could and couldn't do.

walk swim watch run see climb

I could ...

1 ________

2 ________

I couldn't ...

1 ________

2 ________

4 Read. Then write.

1 He hiked ____ (hike) through the mountains yesterday.

2 She ________ (climb) a tree in the rainforest last summer.

3 I ________ (watch) the gorillas last week.

4 They ________ (walk) to school last Monday.

Unit 7

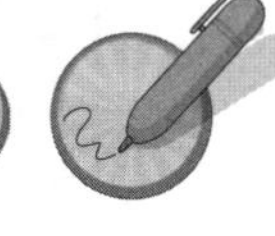

1 Write the words in alphabetical order.

crying shouting yawning frowning laughing ~~blushing~~ smiling shaking drinking

1 blushing 2 ______ 3 ______
4 ______ 5 ______ 6 ______
7 ______ 8 ______ 9 ______

2 Write.

angry ~~nervous~~ blushing feel

1 Tests make her nervous.
2 My friend is ______ because he's embarrassed.
3 I'm shouting because I'm ______.
4 How do you feel? I ______ relieved.

3 Read. Then write the questions.

1 Why are you crying? I'm crying because I'm sad.
2 ______? She's nervous because she has a test.
3 ______? He's shouting because he's angry.
4 ______? I'm embarrassed.

4 Read. Then write your answers.

1 What makes you feel nervous? ______
2 What makes you feel proud? ______
3 What makes you feel relaxed? ______
4 What makes you feel worried? ______

Unit 8

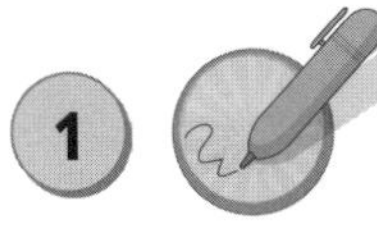

1 Write the words in alphabetical order.

scuba diving snorkelling hang gliding kayaking fishing ~~bungee jumping~~ rafting horse-riding rock climbing

1 bungee jumping 2 ______ 3 ______

4 ______ 5 ______ 6 ______

7 ______ 8 ______ 9 ______

2 Read. Then write.

1

A: Let's go snorkelling.

B: Great idea. I love snorkelling.

2

A: ______

B: Sorry, I don't like hang gliding.

3

A: Have you got riding boots?

B: No, ______.

4

A: ______

B: Yes, I have. I've got a fishing rod.

3 Read. Then write your answers.

1 What are you going to do tomorrow morning? ______

______

2 What are you going to do next week? ______

______

3 What are you going to do next summer? ______

______

Picture dictionary

Unit 1

Leisure activities

skiing

cooking

watching TV

playing the guitar

playing computer games

skateboarding

chatting online

skipping

painting

playing hockey

reading magazines

watching films

surfing the internet

walking the dog

riding a scooter

Special houses

lighthouse

stairs

sea

Unit 2

Wild animals/food

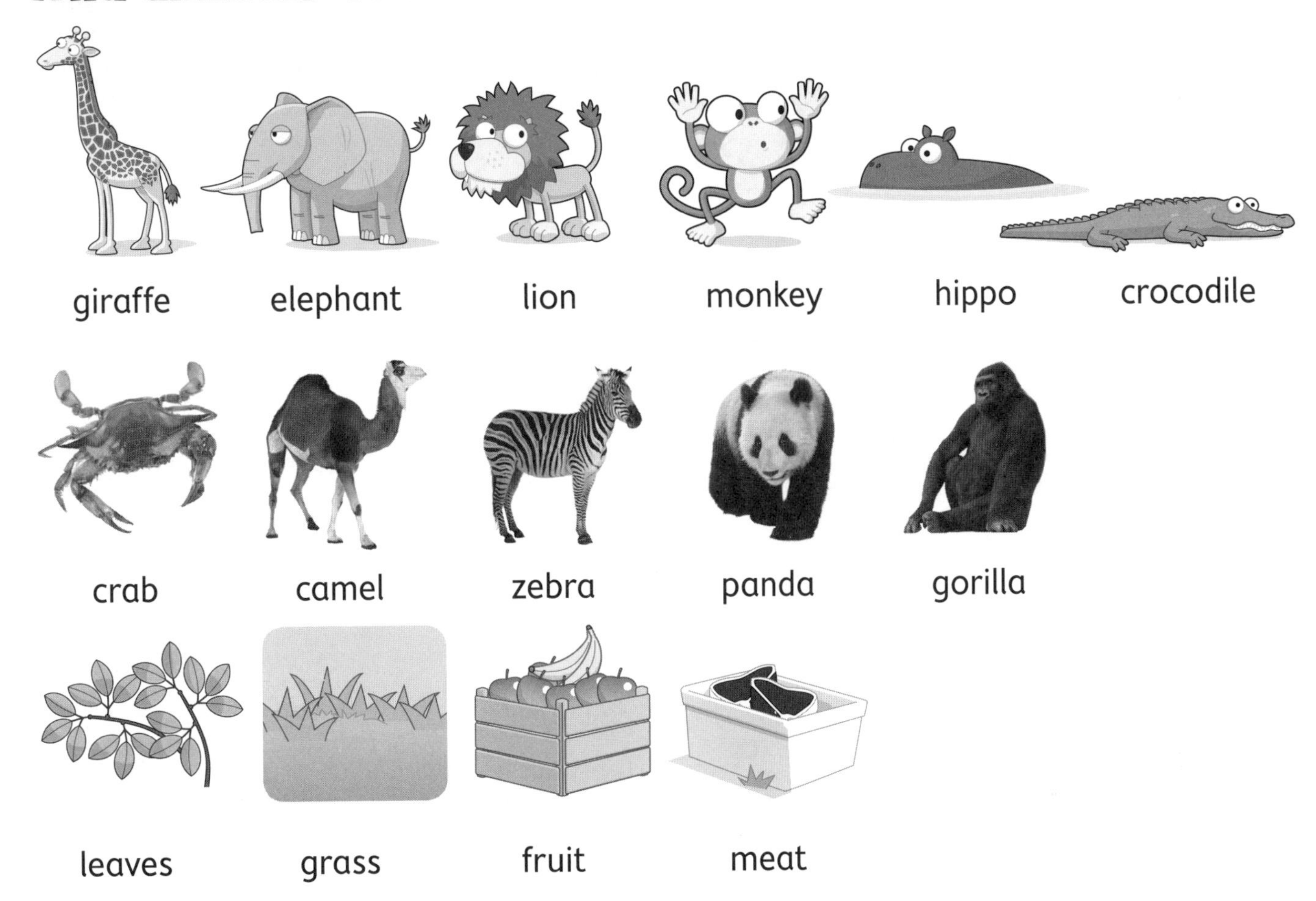

giraffe elephant lion monkey hippo crocodile

crab camel zebra panda gorilla

leaves grass fruit meat

Habitats

river

desert

grassland

forest

rainforest

The food chain

herbivore

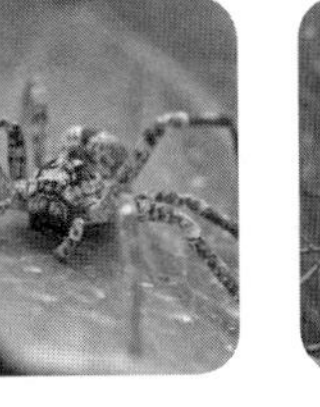
carnivore

omnivore

grasshopper

mouse

snake

eagle

Unit 3

Weather

warm

humid

wet

stormy

lightning

thunder

temperature

degrees

Seasonal activities

go camping

go water skiing

go hiking

go snowboarding

Seasons

spring

summer

autumn

winter

Hurricanes

hurricane
(or cyclone or typhoon)

wave

Unit 4

Activities

have music lessons

have ballet lessons

do karate

do gymnastics

practise the piano

practise the violin

learn to draw

learn to cook

study English

study Maths

Time

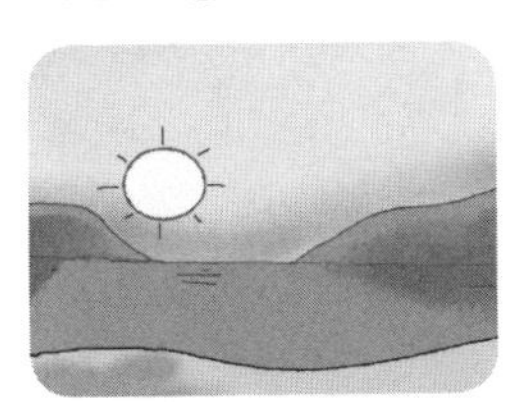
morning

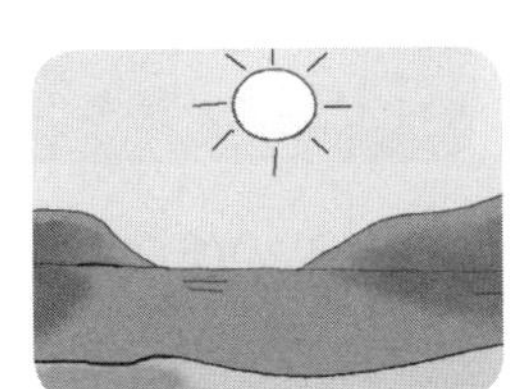
midday

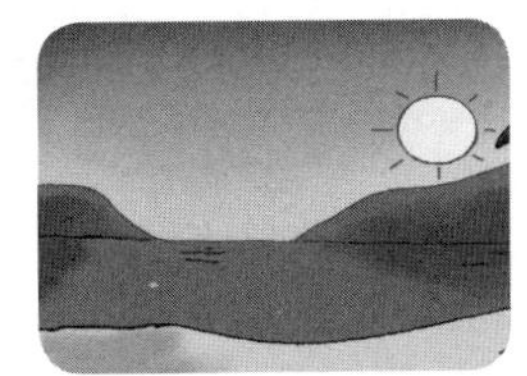
afternoon

evening

2.15
quarter past 2

2.30
half past 2

2.45
quarter to 3

Going to school

road

plane

snowmobile

Unit 5

Jobs

builder

firefighter

police officer

basketball player

film star

ballet dancer

astronaut

singer

model

journalist

photographer

carpenter

mechanic

lawyer

athlete

fashion designer

computer programmer

Kids' Forum

champion

coach

train

famous

brave

Unit 6

Nature

hut bridge cave waterfall valley mountain

path nest vines lake sea coast hills

Prepositions

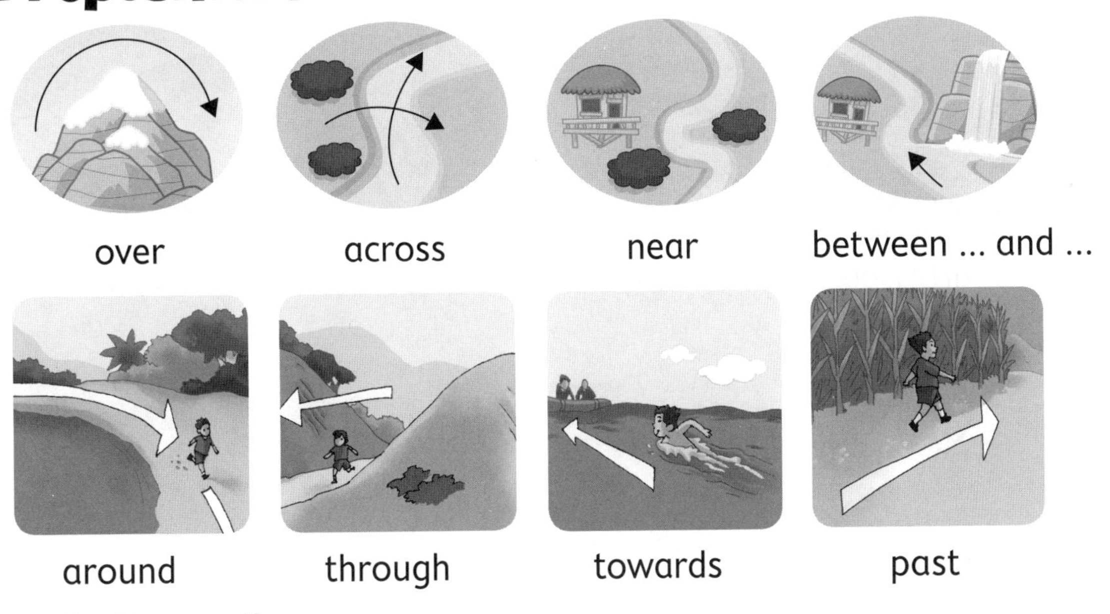

over across near between ... and ...

around through towards past

Rainforest

parrot hummingbird nectar tapir giant tarantula

Unit 7

Actions/Emotions

Unit 8

Outdoor activities and equipment

snorkelling

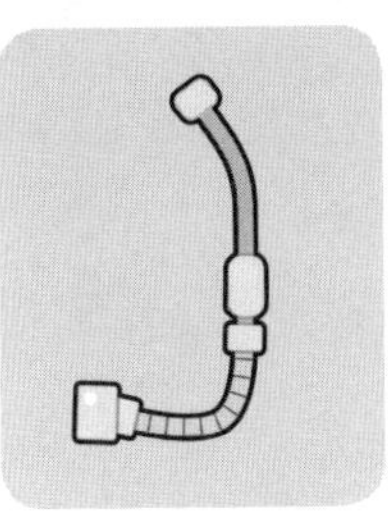
snorkel

surfing

surfboard

sailing

life jacket

kayaking

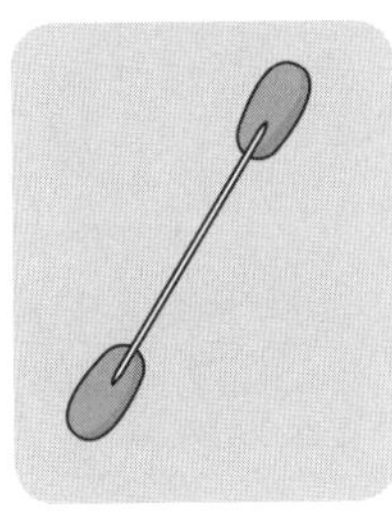
paddle

fishing

fishing rod

horse-riding

riding boots

Emotions

fond of

crazy about

bored with

scared of

terrified of

Extreme sports

rafting

bungee jumping

rock climbing

scuba diving

hang gliding

Coral reefs

coral reef

seahorse

sea snake

starfish

butterfly fish

parrotfish

Pearson Education Limited
Edinburgh Gate
Harlow
Essex CM20 2JE
England
and Associated Companies throughout the world.

Poptropica® English Islands

Editorial and project management by hyphen

First published 2017
Seventeenth impression 2022
ISBN: 978-1-2921-9856-9

Set in Fiendstar 16/21pt
Printed in Neografia, Slovakia

Acknowledgements: The publisher would like to thank Viv Lambert, Anne Feunteun, Debbie Peters, Aaron Jolly and José Luis Morales, Steve Elsworth and Jim Rose for their contributions to this edition.

Illustrators: Humberto Blanco (Sylvie Poggio Artists Agency), Anja Boretzki (Good Illustration), Chan Cho Fai, Lee Cosgrove, Leo Cultura, Marek Jagucki, Jim Peacock (Beehive Illustration), Mark Ruffle (The Organisation), and Yam Wai Lun

Picture Credits: The publisher would like to thank the following for their kind permission to reproduce their photographs:

(Key: b-bottom; c-centre; l-left; r-right; t-top)

123RF.com: 24c, 104 (surfing internet), 106bc, 111 (sea snake), Jacek Chabraszewski 14t, Lajos Endredi 109 (tapir), Goodluz 108cl, Thomas Gowanlock 104bc, Anton Oparin 108tc, Wavebreak Media Ltd 108c, Cathy Yeulet 104 (painting), Hongqi Zhang 108tr; **Alamy Stock Photo:** A Room With Views 104tr, Age Fotostock 24t, Roger Bamber 74cr, Blend Images 104cr, Caia Image 74cl, Design Pics Inc 104tl, Dpa Picture Alliance 54cr, Robert Harding 14cl, Image Source Plus 104 (hockey), Imagebroker 14cr, Jose Manuel Revuelta Luna 64r, NASA Archive 106bl; **Fotolia.com:** Kaspars Grinvalds 108tl, Maridav 108br, Maska82 34r, Tyler Olson 104cl, A Rochau 111tc, Lurii Sokolov 104 (walking dog), SolisImages 108 (computer programmer), Syda Productions 108 (carpenter), Tarasov_Vl 107bl, UTBP 111tr; **Photolibrary.com:** 108bc; **Shutterstock.com:** 2009fotofriends 109tl, 105bc, 111bl, S Bakhadirov 107br, Arvind Balaraman 109bc, Wojciech Beczynski 107bc, Joe Belanger 111 (seahorse), Mircea Bezergheanu 111 (starfish), Rich Carey 104br, 111 (scuba divers), Chesapeake Images 109 (hummingbird), Cigdem Sean Cooper 111br, elnavegante 105 (desert), Vladislav Gajic 111 (butterfly fish), Janne Hamalainen 105cl, India Picture 108bl, Eric Isselee 105 (camel), 105 (panda), 105tc, 105tr, Ammit Jack 111tl, Michael Jung 44, Iakov Kalinin 109tc (sea), Karriekeeshen 64l, Cathy Keifer 109br, Henrik Lehnerer 109bl, Doug Lemke 104bl, Anatoliy Lukich 105br, Stephen Mcsweeny 108cr, Christopher Meder 105cr, N K. 109tr, Vitalii Nesterchuk 111 (bungee jumping), Sergey Novikov 34l, Pakhnyushchy 105 (forest), Platslee 109tc (coast), Slaven 108 (fashion designer), wavebreakmedia 108 (lawyer), Feng Yu 105tl, Oleg Znamenskiy 105c, Zuzule 105bl

Cover images: *Back:* **Fotolia.com:** frender r; **Shutterstock.com:** Denys Prykhodov l